Success guides

Standard Grade
Chemistry

Archie Gibb × Emma Poole

Contents

Chemical reactions

Atoms and covalent bonding

Formulae and equations

Ionic bonding and ionic formulae

Hydrocarbons and fuels

Acids, alkalis and salts

Making electricity: electrochemical cells

Metals and corrosion

Plastics and synthetic fibres

Making Fertilisers

Carbohydrates to alcohol

Calculations

Elements, compounds and mixtures

Elements

Everything in the world is made from just over 100 elements. Every element is made up of very small particles called **atoms.** An **element** is a substance made up of one type of atom.

The names, symbols and atomic numbers of the different elements are given in the Periodic Table on page 8 of your Data Booklet:

- Magnesium is an element and it has the symbol, Mg. All magnesium atoms are the same.
- Oxygen is another element. It has the symbol, O. All oxygen atoms are the same but are different from magnesium atoms.

Top Tip
Remember that the Periodic Table in your Data Booklet has the names and symbols of the elements.

Compounds

Compounds are formed when elements react together. A **compound** contains two or more elements joined together. For example, magnesium oxide is a compound formed when the elements magnesium and oxygen react together. You may have seen magnesium burning in air. When this happens the magnesium is reacting with the oxygen in the air.

Magnesium burning in air with a very bright white light

The **word equation** that describes this reaction is:

magnesium + oxygen → magnesium oxide

        elements   compound

Compounds with names ending in **-ide** contain the two elements indicated in the name. Magnesium ox**ide**, MgO, contains the two elements magnesium and oxygen.

Compounds with names ending in **-ate** or **-ite** also contain the element oxygen. Sodium carbon**ate**, Na_2CO_3, contains the elements sodium, carbon **and oxygen**.

Top Tip
Remember: if the name of the compound ends in -ite or -ate, then the compound also contains oxygen.

Mixtures

When two substances are mixed together but don't actually react with each other we say that a **mixture** has been formed. Common mixtures include air and crude oil. Air is a mixture of nitrogen, oxygen and other gases. Crude oil is a mixture of different hydrocarbons.

Solutions

When a **solute** dissolves in a **solvent** a **solution** is formed. A solution is a mixture, because the solute has not reacted with the solvent when it dissolves.

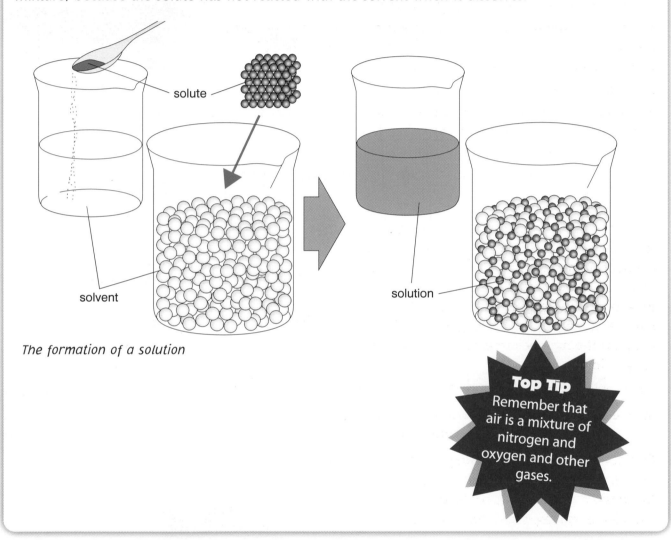

solute

solvent

solution

The formation of a solution

Top Tip
Remember that air is a mixture of nitrogen and oxygen and other gases.

Quick Test

1. Write down the symbols for the following elements:
   magnesium, chlorine, copper, iron, silver

2. Which elements are present in:
   copper oxide, zinc carbonate, sodium sulphite, potassium nitrate, sodium chloride, sodium chlorate?

3. What is the difference between a compound and a mixture?

Identifying chemical reactions

When a chemical reaction takes place a new substance is formed. The substances at the start of the reaction are known as the **reactants** and the new substances are known as the **products**.

What to look for in a reaction

Three things that indicate a chemical reaction has taken place include:

- a colour change

- a precipitate forming

Top Tip
Remember that a precipitate is the solid formed when two liquids are mixed together.

- a gas being given off

Exothermic and endothermic reactions

Sometimes you cannot see any change when a chemical reaction takes place but there may be an energy change such as a change in temperature.

20° C   20° C   27° C

acid   alkali

An acid reacting with an alkali to produce an increase in temperature

Top Tip
You should recognise that a chemical reaction is taking place if you see
*bubbles
*a colour change
*a precipitate forming
*that heat has been given out or taken in.

A reaction in which heat is given out is **exothermic** (heat given out). If the temperature had dropped the reaction would be **endothermic** (heat taken in)

Quick Test

1. Which of the changes below are chemical reactions?
   a) melting ice
   b) breaking glass
   c) frying an egg
   d) hydrogen produced when magnesium is added to acid
   e) adding water to orange juice
   f) iron rusting
   g) separating alcohol from water by distilling
   h) filtering sand from water.

2. What does exothermic mean?

Answers 1. c, d and f. **2.** Heat energy is given out.

Rates of reaction

Key Fact Rates of reaction can be slow or fast

← rusting   explosions →

Analysing rates of reaction

The rate of a chemical reaction can be measured by:
- how fast the **products** are being made
- how fast the **reactants** are being used up.

The graph (at right) shows the amount of product made in three experiments.

The graph is **steepest** at the start of the reaction for all three experiments; it then starts to **level out** as the reactant particles get used up.

When the graph becomes level, the reaction has finished. The graph shows that **Experiment 2** is faster than **Experiment 1**.

This could have been due to Experiment 2 having a higher temperature, a greater concentration of reactant particles (or pressure for gases), a greater surface area or a catalyst being added to it.

Experiments 1 and 2 make the **same amount** of the product so they both had the same amounts of reactants at the start of the reaction.

In Experiment 3 only **half** as much product was made.

This shows that there were less reactants at the start of Experiment 3.

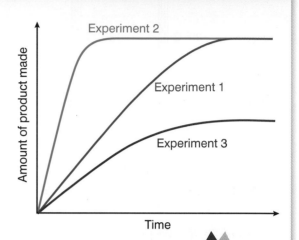

Top Tip
When analysing graphs remember:
*the steeper the slope the faster is the reaction
*the reaction is over when the graph levels out.

Increasing the surface area

The greater the **surface area**, the more chance of collisions occurring, so the faster the rate of reaction.

 small surface area (larger pieces)

 large surface area (smaller pieces)

Top Tip
Remember: small pieces have a larger overall surface area.

Temperature

If the temperature is increased, particles move quicker. Increasing the temperature increases the **rate** of **reaction** because the particles collide more often and with more energy so there are more successful collisions, and the rate increases.

*a **low temperature** slows down reaction rate.*

*a **high temperature** speeds up reaction rate.*

Increasing the concentration of dissolved reactants

The **greater** the concentration, the **more** reactant particles there are in the solution. There will be more collisions and so the reaction rate is increased.

low concentration of particles

high concentration of particles

Concentrated acid will react more quickly than dilute acid.

Adding a catalyst

- A catalyst increases the rate of reaction, but is not itself used up in the reaction.
- Catalysts are specific to certain reactions.
- An everyday example of a catalyst is platinum and other transition metals inside the catalytic converters in car exhausts.

Quick Test

1. What happens to the rate of a reaction if the temperature is decreased?

2. What happens to the rate of a reaction if the concentration of the dissolved reactants is increased?

3. What happens to the rate of a reaction if the surface area of a reactant is increased?

4. What does a catalyst do to the rate of reaction?

5. Why can catalysts be reused?

6. How can the rate of a chemical reaction be measured?

7. Give four ways in which you could increase the rate of a chemical reaction.

8. Give three ways in which you could decrease the rate of a chemical reaction.

Answers 1. Decreases **2.** Increases **3.** Increases **4.** A catalyst increases the rate of reaction **5.** Not used up during the reaction **6.** How fast reactant used up/product is made **7.** Increase temperature; increase concentration; increase surface area; add a catalyst **8.** Decrease temperature; decrease concentration; decrease surface area

Classifying elements

Solids, liquids or gases?

Most chemical elements are **solid** at room temperature. Some elements exist as **gases** but only two elements, mercury (Hg) and bromine (Br) are **liquid** at room temperature. The state at room temperature (approximately 25 °C) can be determined by looking at the **melting and boiling points** of the elements on page 3 of the Data Booklet.

- If 25 °C is above the melting point of the element, then the element is a solid at room temperature.
- If 25 °C is between the melting and boiling points of the element, then the element is a liquid at room temperature.
- If 25 °C is above the boiling point of the element, then the element is a gas at room temperature.

Top Tip
Make sure you know where you can find information in your Data Booklet. It is a very useful examination resource.

Metals or non-metals?

Three-quarters of the elements in the Periodic Table are **metals.** Elements shown at the left-hand side of the dark zig-zag line on the Periodic Table are metals, except for hydrogen, element number 1, which is a non-metal. This is seen on the Periodic Table opposite. This is the same as the Periodic Table on page 8 of the Data Booklet.

Naturally occurring or made by scientists?

Most elements are found naturally either as the element or in compounds. The elements after uranium (number 92) have been made by scientists and do not occur naturally. These can be seen on the Periodic Table opposite.

Quick Test

1. Name and write the symbol for the only metal which is not solid at room temperature.
2. Which other element is liquid at room temperature?
3. Which three elements in Group 4 are metals?
4. Which element in Group 5 is a gas at room temperature?
5. In which group are all the elements gases?
6. Name two elements that are not naturally occurring and have been made by scientists.
7. Name an element in Group 7 that is solid at room temperature.
8. Which two elements in Group 7 are gases at room temperature?
9. Use the Periodic Table to find out what you can about sodium and xenon.

Answers 1. Mercury (Hg). **2.** Bromine (Br). **3.** Germanium (Ge), tin (Sn) and lead (Pb). **4.** Nitrogen. **5.** Group 0: the noble gases. **6.** Any with atomic number greater than 92. **7.** Iodine. **8.** Fluorine and chlorine. **9.** Sodium has the symbol Na. It is a naturally occurring metal that is solid at room temperature. Xenon has the symbol Xe. It is a naturally occurring gas. It is a non-metal.

Periodic table of the elements.

Key

Atomic number
Name of element
Symbol
Melting point °C
Boiling point °C

- naturally occurring
- gases
- liquid
- made by scientists

transition metals

metals

non-metals

Group 1
Group 2
Group 3
Group 4
Group 5
Group 6
Group 7
Group 0

* at 28 atmospheres
† sublimes

1 Hydrogen **H** −259 *−253*			2 Helium **He** −272 *−269*

| 3 Lithium **Li** 181 *1347* | 4 Beryllium **Be** 1278 *2970** | 5 Boron **B** 2300 *4000* | 6 Carbon **C** 3642† | 7 Nitrogen **N** −210 *−196* | 8 Oxygen **O** −218 *−183* | 9 Fluorine **F** −220 *−188* | 10 Neon **Ne** −249 *−246* |

| 11 Sodium **Na** 98 *883* | 12 Magnesium **Mg** 649 *1090* | 13 Aluminium **Al** 660 *2467* | 14 Silicon **Si** 1410 *2355* | 15 Phosphorus **P** 44 *280* | 16 Sulphur **S** 113 *445* | 17 Chlorine **Cl** −101 *−35* | 18 Argon **Ar** −189 *−186* |

| 19 Potassium **K** 63 *759* | 20 Calcium **Ca** 842 *1484* | 21 Scandium **Sc** 1541 *2831* | 22 Titanium **Ti** 1660 *3287* | 23 Vanadium **V** 1890 *3380* | 24 Chromium **Cr** 1857 *2672* | 25 Manganese **Mn** 1244 *1962* | 26 Iron **Fe** 1535 *2750* | 27 Cobalt **Co** 1495 *2927* | 28 Nickel **Ni** 1453 *2913* | 29 Copper **Cu** 1083 *2567* | 30 Zinc **Zn** 420 *907* | 31 Gallium **Ga** 30 *2403* | 32 Germanium **Ge** 937 *2830* | 33 Arsenic **As** 817* *613†* | 34 Selenium **Se** 217 *685* | 35 Bromine **Br** −7 *59* | 36 Krypton **Kr** −157 *−152* |

| 37 Rubidium **Rb** 39 *688* | 38 Strontium **Sr** 769 *1384* | 39 Yttrium **Y** 1522 *3338* | 40 Zirconium **Zr** 1852 *4377* | 41 Niobium **Nb** 2477 *4742* | 42 Molybdenum **Mo** 2623 *4639* | 43 Technetium **Tc** 2157 *4265* | 44 Ruthenium **Ru** 2310 *3900* | 45 Rhodium **Rh** 1966 *3695* | 46 Palladium **Pd** 1552 *2963* | 47 Silver **Ag** 962 *2212* | 48 Cadmium **Cd** 321 *765* | 49 Indium **In** 157 *2080* | 50 Tin **Sn** 232 *2602* | 51 Antimony **Sb** 631 *1750* | 52 Tellurium **Te** 452 *988* | 53 Iodine **I** 114 *184* | 54 Xenon **Xe** −112 *−107* |

| 55 Caesium **Cs** 28 *671* | 56 Barium **Ba** 725 *1640* | 57 Lanthanum **La** 921 *3457* | 72 Hafnium **Hf** 2227 *4602* | 73 Tantalum **Ta** 2996 *5425* | 74 Tungsten **W** 3410 *5660* | 75 Rhenium **Re** 3180 *5627* | 76 Osmium **Os** 3033 *5012* | 77 Iridium **Ir** 2410 *4130* | 78 Platinum **Pt** 1772 *3827* | 79 Gold **Au** 1064 *2856* | 80 Mercury **Hg** −39 *357* | 81 Thallium **Tl** 304 *1457* | 82 Lead **Pb** 328 *1749* | 83 Bismuth **Bi** 271 *1560* | 84 Polonium **Po** 254 *962* | 85 Astatine **At** 302 | 86 Radon **Rn** −71 *−62* |

| 87 Francium **Fr** − *−* | 88 Radium **Ra** 725 *1640* | 89 Actinium **Ac** − *−* |

58–71

90–103

| 57 Lanthanum **La** | 58 Cerium **Ce** | 59 Praseodymium **Pr** | 60 Neodymium **Nd** | 61 Promethium **Pm** | 62 Samarium **Sm** | 63 Europium **Eu** | 64 Gadolinium **Gd** | 65 Terbium **Tb** | 66 Dysprosium **Dy** | 67 Holmium **Ho** | 68 Erbium **Er** | 69 Thulium **Tm** | 70 Ytterbium **Yb** | 71 Lutetium **Lu** |

| 89 Actinium **Ac** | 90 Thorium **Th** | 91 Protactinium **Pa** | 92 Uranium **U** | 93 Neptunium **Np** | 94 Plutonium **Pu** | 95 Americium **Am** | 96 Curium **Cm** | 97 Berkelium **Bk** | 98 Californium **Cf** | 99 Einsteinium **Es** | 100 Fermium **Fm** | 101 Mendelevium **Md** | 102 Nobelium **No** | 103 Lawrencium **Lr** |

Some families in the Periodic Table

The Periodic Table

- In the modern Periodic Table the elements are arranged in order of increasing atomic number.
- The elements are placed in rows so that elements with similar properties are in the same column.
- These vertical columns are called **groups**.
- All the members of a group share similar properties.
- The horizontal rows are called **periods**.

Top Tip
Elements in the same group have similar chemical properties.

Group 1: The alkali metals

Top Tip
The alkali metals are very reactive metals and must be stored under oil.

Examples: **lithium**, **sodium**, **potassium**

The alkali metals show these properties:

- They have **lower densities** than water and are quite soft compared to other metals.
- They have **low melting points** compared with other metals.
- They **react vigorously** with water, releasing **hydrogen gas** and forming **alkaline solutions**.

The Group 1 metals react with non-metals to form white, ionic compounds which **dissolve** to form colourless solutions.

The transition metals

Examples: **iron**, **nickel** and **copper**

- Transition metals are **hard** and **strong**.
- They are much **less reactive** than the metals in Group 1 and do not react quickly with oxygen or water.
- Transition metals are widely used.
- Iron is often used as a **structural material**.
- Copper is a good conductor of both heat and electricity, and it is often used for electrical cables.
- Transition metals form coloured compounds which can be used in pottery glazes.
- Many transition metals and their compounds can act as catalysts. Iron and platinum are widely used in this way.

Group 7: The halogens

Fluorine

- Fluorine is a **very poisonous**, pale yellow gas.

Chlorine

- Chlorine is a **poisonous**, pale green gas.
- Chlorine is used in water purification and bleaching.

Bromine

- Bromine is a **poisonous**, dense, brown **liquid**.

Iodine

- Iodine is a dark grey, crystalline **solid** or a purple vapour.
- Iodine solution is used as an antiseptic.

5	6	7	0
			He 2
O 8	F 9	Ne 10	
S 16	Cl 17	Ar 18	
Se 34	Br 35	Kr 36	
Te 52	I 53	Xe 54	
Po 84	At 85	Rn 86	

Down the group each element becomes less reactive.
The halogens have coloured vapours.
Down the group the colour of the vapour gets darker.

- Melting and boiling points increase down the group (the first two are gases, the next – bromine – is a liquid, and iodine is a solid).
- All the halogens are poisonous and should only be used in a fume cupboard.
- Halogens react with metals to form compounds.
- Halogens can also **react with non-metals** to form **covalently bonded compounds**.

Top Tip
The halogens are the most reactive non-metal elements.

Quick Test

1. What are the vertical columns in the Periodic Table called?
2. Give three examples of alkali metals.
3. Why do alkali metals float on water?
4. Why are alkali metals stored under oil?
5. Which gas is released when alkali metals react with water?
6. Name three transition metals.
7. Give two uses of transition metals.
8. What is the name given to the Group 7 elements?
9. Which is the most reactive element in Group 7?
10. What is chlorine used for?

Group 0: the noble gases

Chemical properties of the noble gases

- The noble gases are the elements helium, neon, argon, krypton, xenon and radon.
- They are very unreactive gases.
- They are sometimes called 'inert' because they are so unreactive.
- Argon makes up about 1 per cent of dry air.

Trends in the noble gases

As you go down the group:
- density increases;
- boiling point increases.

The noble gases are colourless, monatomic gases (they exist as individual atoms rather than as diatomic molecules as other gases do).

Physical properties of the noble gases

- All the members of Group 0 are **gases at room temperature**.
- If they are **cooled down** they can become **liquids** and eventually **solids**.
- They are poor conductors of both electricity and heat.

Uses of the noble gases

Helium

- Helium is used in **balloons** and in **airships**, because it is **less dense** than air (and **not flammable** like hydrogen).

Argon

- Argon is used in light bulbs (**filament lamps**).
- Surrounding the hot filament with inert argon stops it from burning away.

Neon

- Neon is used in electrical discharge tubes in advertising signs.

Krypton

- Krypton is used in **lasers**.

Quick Test

1. Name and give the symbols for the first three noble gases.

2. How much argon will be present in 1 litre of dry air?

3. What does 'monatomic' mean?

4. What is helium used for?

5. What is argon used for?

6. What is neon used for?

7. Which noble gas has the lowest boiling point?

8. Which noble gas has the greatest density?

Answers 1. Helium (He), Neon (Ne) and Argon (Ar). **2.** 10 cm³. **3.** Existing as individual atoms. **4.** Balloons and airships. **5.** It is the gas inside light bulbs. **6.** Advertising signs. **7.** Helium. **8.** Radon.

Atomic structure

Atoms

Every element is made up of very small particles called **atoms.** Atoms have a very small positively charged **nucleus** with negatively charged **electrons** moving around outside the nucleus. An atom is neutral because the positive charge of the nucleus is equal to the sum of the negatively charged electrons outside the nucleus.

The structure of an atom

An atom has a nucleus surrounded by shells of electrons.

The **electrons** are found in shells around the **nucleus**.

The **nucleus** is found at the centre of the **atom** and contains **neutrons** and **protons**.

Top Tip
Make sure you are familiar with the charge, mass and location of the three types of particles.

Structure of the atom

- **Protons** have a **positive charge** and a **mass of 1.**
- **Neutrons** have **no charge** and also have a **mass of 1.**
- **Electrons** have a **negative charge** and a **negligible mass** (which we take as 0).

Top Tip
Number of neutrons = mass number – atomic number

Information about protons, neutrons and electrons is summarised in the table below:

Particle	Mass	Charge	Location
Proton	1	+1	In the nucleus
Neutron	1	0	In the nucleus
Electrons	0	–1	Outside the nucleus

In all neutral atoms there is no overall charge, so the number of protons is equal to the number of electrons.

23
Na   The **mass number** is the number of protons added to the number of neutrons.
11   The **atomic number** is the number of protons.

- Sodium has an atomic number of 11, so it has 11 protons.
- The sodium atom has no overall charge so the number of electrons must be the same as the number of protons. Sodium therefore has 11 electrons.
- The number of neutrons is given by the mass number minus the atomic number.
- Sodium has 23 – 11 = 12 neutrons.

Isotopes

Isotopes of an element have the **same** number of protons but a **different** number of neutrons. So isotopes have the same **atomic number** but a different **mass number**.

- Chlorine has 2 common isotopes:

$^{35}_{17}$**Cl**
- 17 protons
- 17 electrons
- **18 neutrons**

$^{37}_{17}$**Cl**
- 17 protons
- 17 electrons
- **20 neutrons**

- The isotopes will react chemically in the same way because they have identical numbers of electrons.

- Most elements exist as a mixture of isotopes.

The atomic structure of elements 1–20

Symbol	Elements	Protons	Electrons	Neutrons
$^{1}_{1}$ H	Hydrogen	1	1	0
$^{4}_{2}$ He	Helium	2	2	2
$^{7}_{3}$ Li	Lithium	3	3	4
$^{9}_{4}$ Be	Beryllium	4	4	5
$^{11}_{5}$ B	Boron	5	5	6
$^{12}_{6}$ C	Carbon	6	6	6
$^{14}_{7}$ N	Nitrogen	7	7	7
$^{16}_{8}$ O	Oxygen	8	8	8
$^{19}_{9}$ F	Fluorine	9	9	10
$^{20}_{10}$ Ne	Neon	10	10	10

Symbol	Elements	Protons	Electrons	Neutrons
$^{23}_{11}$ Na	Sodium	11	11	12
$^{24}_{12}$ Mg	Magnesium	12	12	12
$^{27}_{13}$ Al	Aluminium	13	13	14
$^{28}_{14}$ Si	Silicon	14	14	14
$^{31}_{15}$ P	Phosphorus	15	15	16
$^{32}_{16}$ S	Sulphur	16	16	16
$^{35}_{17}$ Cl	Chlorine	17	17	18
$^{40}_{18}$ Ar	Argon	18	18	22
$^{39}_{19}$ K	Potassium	19	19	20
$^{40}_{20}$ Ca	Calcium	20	20	20

Quick Test

1. What does the nucleus contain?

2. What are found in shells around the nucleus?

3. What is the charge and mass of a proton?

4. What is the charge and mass of an electron?

5. What is the charge and mass of a neutron?

6. What is the mass number of an atom?

7. What is the atomic number of an atom?

8. What is the same about the atoms of two isotopes of an element?

9. What is different about the atoms of two isotopes of an element?

10. Why do isotopes of an element react in the same way?

11. Calculate the number of protons, neutrons and electrons in $^{63}_{29}$Cu.

Answers 1. Protons and neutrons **2.** Electrons **3.** Charge +1, mass 1 **4.** Charge −1, mass negligible **5.** No charge, mass 1 **6.** Number of protons + number of neutrons **7.** Number of protons **8.** Atomic number/number of protons or electrons **9.** Mass number/number of neutrons **10.** They have the same number of electrons. **11.** 29 protons, 34 neutrons and 29 electrons.

Electron arrangement

Electron arrangement

- Electrons are arranged in energy levels or shells. *CREDIT*
- The first shell may contain up to **2** electrons.
- The second shell contains up to **8** electrons.
- The third shell can hold up to **18** electrons.
- The number of electrons in the outer shell indicates the group that the element belongs to. So, the electron arrangement shows how the atom will react chemically.
- The maximum number of electrons in the **outer shell** is **8**.

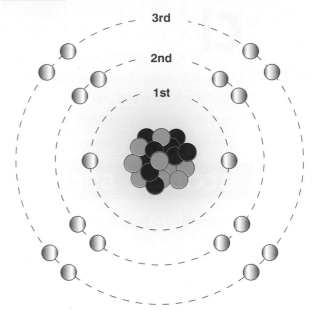

A model of electron shells

Lithium

- Number of protons = 3.
- Number of electrons = 3.
- The electron arrangement is 2, 1.

Magnesium

- Number of protons = 12.
- Number of electrons = 12.
- The electron arrangement is 2, 8, 2.

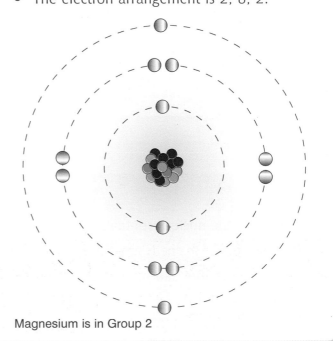

Lithium is in Group 1

Magnesium is in Group 2

The electron arrangement of elements 1–20

Symbol	Element	Electrons	Electron arrangement	Group
H	Hydrogen	1	1	1
He	Helium	2	2	0
Li	Lithium	3	2, 1	1
Be	Beryllium	4	2, 2	2
B	Boron	5	2, 3	3
C	Carbon	6	2, 4	4
N	Nitrogen	7	2, 5	5
O	Oxygen	8	2, 6	6
F	Fluorine	9	2, 7	7
Ne	Neon	10	2, 8	0
Na	Sodium	11	2, 8, 1	1
Mg	Magnesium	12	2, 8, 2	2
Al	Aluminium	13	2, 8, 3	3
Si	Silicon	14	2, 8, 4	4
P	Phosphorus	15	2, 8, 5	5
S	Sulphur	16	2, 8, 6	6
Cl	Chlorine	17	2, 8, 7	7
Ar	Argon	18	2, 8, 8	0
K	Potassium	19	2, 8, 8, 1	1
Ca	Calcium	20	2, 8, 8, 2	2

Top Tip
The number of outer electrons determines the reactivity of the element.

Top Tip
Note that elements with the same number of outer electrons have similar chemical properties. For example, the alkali metals are very reactive as all their atoms have one outer electron.

Quick Test

1. Where are electrons found?

2. How many electrons can the first shell hold?

3. What is the maximum number of electrons in the outer shell of an atom?

4. If an atom has seven protons, how many electrons will it have?

5. Write down the electron arrangement for sodium.

6. How many outer electrons are there in atoms of the alkali metals?

7. How many outer electrons are there in atoms of the halogens?

Answers 1. Around the nucleus in shells or energy levels. **2.** Up to two. **3.** Eight. **4.** Seven. **5.** 2, 8, 1. **6.** One. **7.** Seven.

Chemical formulae

What the chemical formula means

The **chemical formula** shows the number of atoms of each element in a molecule. For example, water has the chemical formula H_2O. This means that each water molecule contains two hydrogen atoms and one oxygen atom joined together.

Chemical formulae you must know

There are some formulae you should get to know. Some of these are shown in the table below.

You should also try to remember the elements that exist as **diatomic elements**.

Top Tip
Chemical formulae are very important. Make sure you can write chemical formulae correctly.

Name	Formula	
Water	H_2O	
Carbon dioxide	CO_2	
Hydrochloric acid	HCl	
Sulphuric acid	H_2SO_4	
Nitric acid	HNO_3	
Sodium hydroxide	NaOH	
Hydrogen	H_2	
Nitrogen	N_2	
Oxygen	O_2	Diatomic elements
Fluorine	F_2	
Chlorine	Cl_2	
Bromine	Br_2	
Iodine	I_2	

Formulae from names of compounds

Sometimes the name of the compound gives information about the formula of that compound. Names of these compounds have prefixes that give the number of atoms of certain elements in each molecule. Prefixes and their meanings are given in the table on the right.

- Carbon monoxide contains one carbon atom joined to one oxygen atom, so it has the formula CO.
- Carbon dioxide contains one carbon atom joined to two oxygen atoms, so it has the formula CO_2.
- Phosphorus pentachloride has the formula PCl_5.
- Dinitrogen tetroxide has the formula N_2O_4.

Prefix	Meaning
mono-	one
di-	two
tri-	three
tetra-	four
penta-	five

Valency

Valency is the combining power of an element. It depends on the number of electrons available for bonding in the outer shell of atoms of that element. Elements in the same group of the Periodic Table will have the same valency as they have the same number of outer electrons.

Valencies of the elements in the different groups in the Periodic Table are shown in the table below. Note that the noble gases have valency of 0. They have no combining power as they are so stable that they do not usually combine with other elements.

Group number	1	2	3	4	5	6	7	0
Valency	1	2	3	4	3	2	1	0

> Using the Periodic Table in your Data Booklet will help you find the valencies of different elements.

The valency is really the number of unpaired electrons in the outer shell of the atoms of that element. Only unpaired electrons are usually available for bonding.

Using your knowledge of the Periodic Table you should be able to work out the valencies of different elements.

- Sodium is in Group 1 and so Na will have valency = 1.
- Carbon is in Group 4, and so C has valency = 4.
- Oxygen is in Group 6 and so O has valency = 2
- The halogens are in Group 7 and so all the halogens have valency = 1.

Quick Test

1. Write down the formulae for the following:
   a) carbon dioxide
   b) hydrochloric acid
   c) fluorine
   d) hydrogen
   e) nitric acid
   f) sulphur trioxide
   g) carbon tetrachloride
   h) nitrogen monoxide
   i) sulphuric acid
   j) sodium hydroxide

2. Write down the valency for
   a) potassium
   b) nitrogen
   c) bromine
   d) argon
   e) calcium
   f) aluminium
   g) sulphur
   h) silicon
   i) phosphorus

Answers 1. a) CO_2 **b)** HCl **c)** F_2 **d)** H_2 **e)** HNO_3 **f)** SO_3 **g)** CCl_4 **h)** NO **i)** H_2SO_4 **j)** NaOH **2. a)** 1 **b)** 3 **c)** 1 **d)** 0 **e)** 2 **f)** 3 **g)** 2 **h)** 4 **i)** 3

Ionic bonding

Key Fact
Ionic bonding involves the transfer of electrons.

How ions are formed

All atoms become more stable if they have a **full outer shell** of electrons (like the noble gases).

Ionic bonding involves the **transfer** of electrons from one atom to another. Metals in Groups I and II – such as sodium and calcium – lose negative electrons to gain a full outer shell. Overall they become positively charged (electrons are negative).

Non-metals in Groups VI and VII – such as oxygen and chlorine – gain negative electrons to attain a full outer shell. So overall they become negatively charged.

The table shows the ions formed by the first 20 elements.

H+ hydrogen								Group 0
								None helium
Group 1	**Group 2**		**Group 3**	**Group 4**	**Group 5**	**Group 6**	**Group 7**	
Li+ lithium	**Be²⁺** beryllium		**None** boron	**None** carbon	**N³⁻** nitride	**O²⁻** oxide	**F⁻** fluoride	**None** neon
Na+ sodium	**Mg²⁺** magnesium		**Al³⁺** aluminium	**None** silicon	**P³⁻** phosphide	**S²⁻** sulphide	**Cl⁻** chloride	**None** argon
K+ potassium	**Ca²⁺** calcium	transition metals						

In neutral atoms there are the **same number** of **positive protons** as there are **negative electrons**. This means that if electrons are lost or gained the number of **protons** and the number of **electrons** is no longer **balanced**. So an ion is an **atom**, or a **small group** of atoms, with a **charge**.

Top Tip
When drawing the dot and cross diagrams to show ionic or covalent bonding, just draw the outer shells.

Examples of ionic compounds

sodium + chlorine → sodium chloride

$$Na + \frac{1}{2}Cl_2 \rightarrow Na^+Cl^-$$

Note: the dots (●) and crosses (×) represent electrons.

The sodium atom **transfers** an electron to the chlorine atom. Both the sodium and the chlorine atoms now have full outer shells. Sodium has lost a negative electron so becomes **positively** charged. Chlorine has **gained** an electron so becomes **negatively** charged. The positive sodium ions are attracted to the negative chloride ions and the ionic compound sodium chloride is made.

sodium + fluorine → sodium fluoride

$$Na + \frac{1}{2}F_2 \rightarrow Na^+F^-$$

Fluorine and chlorine are in the same group of the periodic table, Group 7. Fluorine and sodium will therefore react in a similar way to chlorine and sodium. Sodium transfers one electron to fluorine. The positive sodium ions and negative fluoride ions attract each other and the ionic compound sodium fluoride is formed.

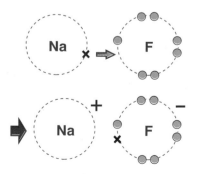

More examples of ionic compounds

Note: the dots (●) and crosses (×) represent electrons.

magnesium + oxygen → magnesium oxide

$$Mg + \tfrac{1}{2}O_2 \rightarrow Mg^{2+}O^{2-}$$

Magnesium transfers two electrons to oxygen. The magnesium atoms become magnesium ions with a 2+ charge. The oxygen atoms become oxide ions with a 2− charge.

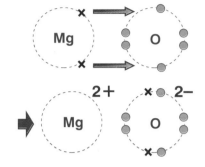

calcium + chlorine → calcium chloride

$$Ca + Cl_2 \rightarrow Ca^{2+}(Cl^-)_2$$

Calcium transfers two electrons in total, one to each chlorine atom. Each calcium ion formed has a 2+ charge. Each chloride ion formed has a 1− charge, so two chloride ions are needed for every calcium ion so that the charges are balanced.

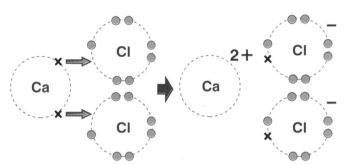

lithium + oxygen → lithium oxide

$$Li + O_2 \rightarrow (Li^+)_2O^{2-}$$

Each lithium atom transfers one electron to the oxygen atom, forming Li^+ and O^{2-} ions.

All these compounds are held together by strong forces of attraction between the oppositely charged ions. Ionic compounds usually contain metal elements joined to non-metal elements.

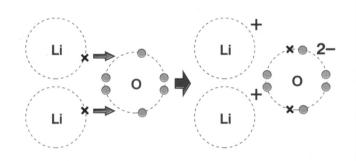

Quick Test

1. If an element in Group I loses an electron, what charge does it have?

2. If an element in Group VI gains two electrons, what charge does it have?

3. Draw a dot and cross diagram to show sodium reacting with chlorine.

4. Draw a dot and cross diagram to show calcium reacting with chlorine.

5. What holds together ionic compounds?

Answers 1. 1+ 2. 2−
3.
4.
5. Strong attraction between oppositely charged ions

Ionic compounds: colours and formulae

Coloured ions

Most ionic compounds are white when solid and dissolve in water to give colourless solutions. However, ions containing **transition metals** are often coloured. The table below shows some examples.

Row	Name of compound	Positive ions present	Negative ions present	Colour
1	sodium chloride	sodium	chloride	colourless
2	copper chloride	copper	chloride	blue
3	sodium chromate	sodium	chromate	yellow
4	potassium nitrate	potassium	nitrate	colourless
5	potassium permanganate	potassium	permanganate	purple
6	sodium sulphate	sodium	sulphate	colourless
7	nickel sulphate	nickel	sulphate	green
8	copper chromate	copper	chromate	green

- If we look at row 1 in the table we can see both sodium and chloride ions must be colourless.
- Remembering that chloride ions are colourless and looking at row 2, we can see that copper ions must be blue.
- If we now look at row 3, it should be obvious that chromate ions must be yellow.
- Copper chromate is coloured green because it contains blue copper ions and yellow chromate ions.

Ion migration

Ion migration experiments such as the one shown below demonstrate that the blue copper ions travel to the negative electrode and the yellow chromate ions travel to the positive electrode. This confirms that copper ions are positively charged and that chromate ions are negatively charged.

negative electrode

positive electrode

blue colour moves towards negative electrode

grains of green copper chromate on filter paper soaked in an electrolyte

yellow colour moves towards positive electrode

an ion migration experiment

Formulae of ions

Metal ions have **positive** charges. The amount of charge depends on the valency of the metal and this depends on the group that the metal belongs to in the Periodic Table. For example, sodium is in Group 1, magnesium is in Group 2 and aluminium is in Group 3 so their ions are Na^+, Mg^{2+} and Al^{3+} respectively.

Ions of non-metal elements usually have negative charges and the amount of charge also depends on the valency of the element. For example, oxygen is a non-metal and has valency = 2, so the oxide ion has a charge of 2– and the formula is O^{2-}. Similarly the chloride ion is Cl^- and the nitride ion is N^{3-}.

Top Tip

Use your Data Booklet to help you write ionic formulae correctly. Pages 4 and 7 give formulae of different ions.

Formulae of ionic compounds

When we write the ionic formulae for compounds the total number of positive charges must be balanced by the total number of negative charges.

- In sodium chloride the sodium ion is Na^+ and this positive charge is balanced by the Cl^- ion. The ionic formula for sodium chloride is Na^+Cl^-.

- The ionic formula for magnesium oxide is $Mg^{2+}O^{2-}$. The 2+ charge on the magnesium ion balances the 2– charge on the oxide ion.

- For sodium oxide the sodium ion is Na^+ and the oxide ion is O^{2-}. Two sodium ions are needed to balance the one oxide ion and the formula is written as $(Na^+)_2O^{2-}$.

Top Tip

You can only write ionic formulae for ionic compounds, not for covalent substances. For example, there is no ionic formula for carbon dioxide.

Quick Test

1. Look at the table on page 36 and deduce the colours of the following ions:
   a) potassium
   b) permanganate
   c) nickel.

2. Predict the colour of nickel chloride.

3. Why does the yellow colour move towards the positive electrode in the ion migration experiment?

4. Write the formulae of the following ions:
   a) potassium
   b) sulphide
   c) fluoride
   d) aluminium.

5. Write ionic formulae for the following compounds:
   a) sodium fluoride
   b) magnesium sulphide
   c) aluminium oxide
   d) calcium chloride
   e) calcium hydroxide.

Fuels

What is a fuel?

A **fuel** is a **chemical** which **burns** to give out **energy**.

a fuel burning and giving off heat

Combustion

When a fuel burns the chemical reaction is known as **combustion**. When combustion takes place the fuel is **reacting with oxygen** from the air and **energy is given out**. This means that combustion is an example of an **exothermic reaction**.

Composition of air

Air is a **mixture** of different gases. Nitrogen is the main component of air. Apart from oxygen, the other gases are mainly argon and carbon dioxide. Air usually contains water vapour as well as these other gases.

Gas	% of dry air
Nitrogen	78
Oxygen	21
Other gases	1

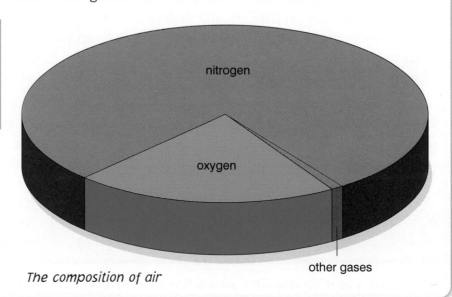

The composition of air

Tests for gases

Oxygen

Oxygen **relights** a glowing **splint**.

glowing splint

O_2 gas

Carbon dioxide

The gas is **bubbled** through **limewater**.
Carbon dioxide turns limewater **cloudy**.

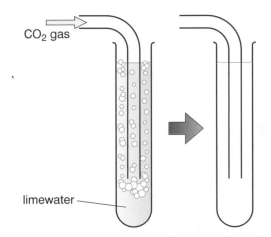

CO_2 gas

limewater

Hydrogen

If a lighted splint is nearby hydrogen will
burn with a '**squeaky pop**'.

'squeaky' pop

H_2 gas

Quick Test

1. What is a *fuel*?

2. What does *combustion* mean?

3. What is meant by an *exothermic* reaction?

4. What percentage of dry air is oxygen?

5. Which gas turns lime water cloudy?

6. Which gas burns with a squeaky pop?

7. What is the test for oxygen gas?

Answers 1. A chemical which burns to give out energy. **2.** Burning. **3.** A reaction which gives out energy. **4.** 21% **5.** Carbon dioxide. **6.** Hydrogen. **7.** It re-lights a glowing splint.

Fossil fuels

Formation of coal, oil and natural gas

Coal, oil and natural gas are fossil fuels.

Fossil fuels are formed over **millions of years**. They are the fossilised remains of dead plants and animals.

Plants and animals died and fell to the sea or swamp floor.

The remains were quickly covered by **sediment**.

In the absence of **oxygen** the remains did not **decay**.

As the layers of sediment **increased** the remains became **heated and pressurised** (squashed).

After millions of years **coal**, **oil** and **natural gas** are formed.

Dead plants falling into swamps form **coal**, while tiny dead sea creatures and plants form **oil and natural gas**.

Burning fossil fuels is an exothermic process – giving out a lot of heat.

Top Tip
Know how fossil fuels are formed and that the original source of their energy is the Sun.

Fossil fuels are **non-renewable**. They take millions of years to form, but they are being used up very quickly.

dead tree

covered in water

lots of layers of sediment slowly build up

hundreds of millions of years later

The build up of dead plant material to form fossil fuels

Fuel crisis

As the human population of the world continues to grow rapidly, fossil fuels are being used up at an alarming rate. Fossil fuels are a **finite resource**. Once they have been used up they **cannot be replaced** as fossil fuels take **hundreds of millions of years to form**. It is difficult to estimate how long fossil fuels will last. **Coal** may last for **300 years**, but **oil and natural gas** are expected to run out in **40–70 years.** To reduce this **fuel crisis**, research in finding and using **alternative fuels** is being carried out. For example, in Brazil **alcohol from sugar cane** is being used as an **alternative to petrol**.

Pollution of the atmosphere

- The burning of fossil fuels can affect the atmosphere.
- Most fuels contain both **carbon** and **hydrogen** and many also contain a little **sulphur**.
- When **carbon** is **burned**, **carbon dioxide** (CO_2) is released into the atmosphere.
- When **hydrogen** is **burned**, **water vapour** (H_2O) is released (water is an **oxide** of hydrogen).
- When **sulphur is burned**, **sulphur dioxide** (SO_2) is formed. Removing sulphur and sulphur compounds from fossil fuels before they are burned reduces air pollution.

Acid rain

- Fossil fuels may contain some **sulphur**.
- When these fuels are burned **sulphur dioxide** is produced and released into the atmosphere.
- This gas dissolves in rainwater to produce **acid rain**.
- Acid rain can affect the environment, damaging statues and buildings as well as trees, animals and plants.

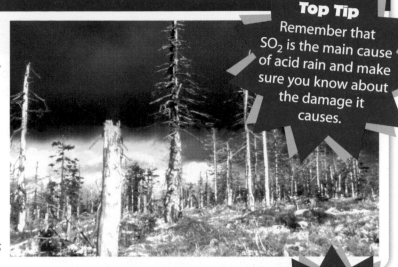

Acid rain kills trees

Top Tip
Remember that SO_2 is the main cause of acid rain and make sure you know about the damage it causes.

Carbon dioxide and the greenhouse effect

- The **greenhouse effect** is slowly heating up the Earth.
- When fossil fuels are burned, **carbon dioxide** is produced.
- Although some of this carbon dioxide is removed from the atmosphere when the gas dissolves in the oceans, the overall amount of carbon dioxide in the atmosphere has **gradually increased** over the last 200 years.
- This carbon dioxide **traps the heat** that has reached the Earth from the Sun.
- Global warming may mean that the ice at the North and South Poles will melt and cause massive flooding.

Top Tip
CO_2 is the main cause of the greenhouse effect.

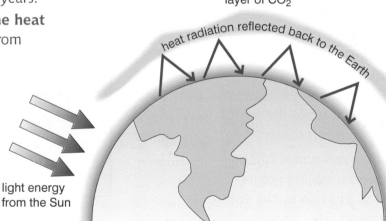

layer of CO_2

heat radiation reflected back to the Earth

light energy from the Sun

The greenhouse effect

Quick Test

1. What is meant by 'a finite resource'?
2. Name the compounds formed when hydrogen, carbon and sulphur are burned.
3. Which gas is thought to be responsible for
   a) the greenhouse effect   **b)** acid rain?
4. Give two examples of the damaging effects of acid rain.

Crude oil

What is crude oil?

Crude oil is a mixture of different **hydrocarbons.** A **hydrocarbon** is a compound containing **only hydrogen and carbon**. The different hydrocarbons present in crude oil have different melting and boiling points. Because these hydrocarbon compounds have different boiling points, they can be separated into **fractions** using **fractional distillation**. A **fraction** is a group of compounds with boiling points within a definite range.

Top Tip
Remember that hydrocarbons contain **only** hydrogen and carbon.

Fractional distillation of crude oil

- Crude oil is a **mixture** of **hydrocarbons.**
- Hydrocarbons are molecules that contain only **hydrogen** and **carbon atoms**.
- Some of the hydrocarbons have **very short chains** of carbon atoms.
- These hydrocarbons are **runny, easy to ignite** and have **low boiling points**.
- Other hydrocarbons have much longer chains of carbon atoms. These hydrocarbons are more **viscous** (less runny), **harder to ignite** and have **higher boiling points**.
- This means that long chain hydrocarbons are **not useful as fuels**.

Fractional distillation can be used to separate mixtures of **hydrocarbons (crude oil)**. In the fractionating column the bottom is kept very hot, while the top of the column is much cooler.

The **smallest molecules** (those with the lowest boiling points) boil off first and **rise to the top of the column**. The other **fractions** are collected at different points down the column.

fuel gas

40°C   petrol (gasoline)

110°C   naphtha

180°C   paraffin (kerosine)

250°C   diesel

340°C   oil

crude oil

bitumen

Fractional distillation of oil

The **fraction** which collects **at the top of the column** has the **lowest boiling point** and so evaporates easiest. It is also the most flammable fraction and is the least viscous. **Bitumen** is the most difficult to evaporate and collects at the bottom of the column. It is the least flammable and the most viscous (thickest liquid). The **fraction** which collects **at the top** of the column has the **smallest molecules** whereas the biggest molecules are present in bitumen. **Bigger molecules have higher boiling points** than smaller molecules as they require more energy to move about rapidly.

Fractions and their uses

The actual composition of the crude oil will depend on the source of the oil. For example, North Sea oil will be slightly different from South American oil. The table below shows a possible result from fractional distillation.

Fraction	Boiling point range (°C)	Number of carbon atoms	Uses
Fuel gases	−160 to 20	1–4	Fool for cooking and heating
Petrol (gasoline)	20 to 75	5–10	Fuel for cars
Naphtha	75 to 130	8–12	Chemicals
Paraffin (kerosene)	130 to 240	10–16	Aviation fuel, heating
Diesel oil	240 to 300	15–28	Fuel for diesel engines in lorries, trains and other vehicles
Lubricating oils and waxes	300 to 350	26–70	Lubricating oils, polishes
Bitumen	Above 350	More than 70	Roads and roofing

Top Tip
You should know a use for each of the fractions.

Quick Test

1. What is meant by a *hydrocarbon*?
2. What is a *fraction*?
3. Why can the different hydrocarbons in crude oil be separated by fractional distillation?
4. Which fraction is the most flammable?
5. Which fraction is the most viscous?
6. Which are smaller, molecules in petrol or molecules in paraffin?
7. What is diesel oil used for?
8. What is bitumen used for?
9. The hydrocarbon, butane, has the molecular formula C_4H_{10}. In which fraction will butane be found?
10. Which fraction has the smallest molecules?

Answers 1. A compound containing **only** hydrogen and carbon. **2.** A group of compounds with similar boiling points. **3.** Because they have different boiling points. **4.** Fuel gases. **5.** Bitumen. **6.** Molecules in petrol. **7.** Fuel for trains. **8.** Roads and roofing. **9.** Fuel gases. **10.** Fuel gases.

Combustion of hydrocarbons

Complete combustion

Top Tip
Make sure you can draw this diagram accurately. Look carefully at the lengths of the tubing inside the test tubes.

When **hydrocarbons burn** they are reacting with oxygen in the air. If there is an **adequate supply of oxygen** the **hydrocarbons burn completely** (complete combustion) producing **carbon dioxide and water.** This can be demonstrated by carrying out the experiment shown below.

to suction pump

ice and water

hydrocarbon burning   water condensing   limewater turns cloudy

Experiment to demonstrate the effects of burning hydrocarbons

- The liquid collected in the first test tube **freezes at 0 ºC** and **boils at 100 ºC** and so must be **water**.
- The **lime water** in the second test tube turns **cloudy** and so **carbon dioxide** must also have been formed by the burning hydrocarbon.

- As carbon dioxide is produced we can say that there must be carbon present in the fuel. The carbon in the carbon dioxide must have come from the fuel.
- As water is produced we can say that there must be hydrogen present in the fuel. The hydrogen in the water must have come from the fuel.
- The oxygen present in the carbon dioxide and in the water will have come from the air.

Incomplete combustion

If there is not enough oxygen present, then, as well as water forming, the other products of combustion may be **carbon (soot)** and the very poisonous **carbon monoxide (CO)** instead of carbon dioxide. This is known as **incomplete combustion.**

The carbon monoxide formed leads to another form of **air pollution**. Carbon monoxide stops the blood carrying oxygen around the body and so is very toxic.

Reducing air pollution

There is a limited supply of oxygen inside a car engine and the burning petrol may produce carbon monoxide. To reduce the amount of carbon monoxide going into the air, car manufacturers now install a **catalytic converter** into the exhaust systems of cars. This converts the poisonous carbon monoxide into the less harmful carbon dioxide.

CREDIT

Increasing the air to fuel ratio (or decreasing the fuel to air ratio) allows more complete combustion to take place inside petrol engines. The more air there is present compared to petrol then the less chance of carbon monoxide being produced and the more efficient the combustion.

Top Tip
Remember that a catalytic converter turns pollutant gases into harmless gases.

A hot spark from the spark plug ignites the petrol inside the engine. The energy from this spark enables the nitrogen in the air to react with the oxygen. The result of this reaction is a mixture of different oxides of nitrogen such as NO and NO_2. These are also poisonous gases. The catalytic converter will turn these gases back into harmless nitrogen and oxygen. The catalytic converter will also change any hydrocarbons that have not burned inside the engine into harmless water and carbon dioxide.

Petrol used to contain compounds of lead so that it would burn smoothly inside car engines. These lead compounds also caused air pollution, so petrol is now lead free.

Quick Test

1. What are the products when a hydrocarbon burns in a plentiful supply of air?

2. What are the products of incomplete combustion of a hydrocarbon fuel?

3. What is the test for water?

4. Write the chemical formula for carbon monoxide.

5. Draw a diagram to show that a burning candle produces carbon monoxide and water.

6. What causes nitrogen and oxygen in air to combine inside a car engine?

7. What does a catalytic converter do?

8. How does changing the fuel to air ratio lead to less carbon monoxide being produced?

Answers 1. CO_2 and H_2O **2.** Carbon (soot), carbon monoxide and water. **3.** It freezes at 0 °C and boils at 100 °C. **4.** CO **5.** See diagram opposite. **6.** The energy from the spark which is used to ignite the petrol. **7.** It converts pollutant gases into harmless gases. **8.** Decreasing the fuel to air ratio means that there will be more oxygen compared to fuel and so more complete combustion will take place.

Alkanes

The alkane family

The **alkanes** are a series of **hydrocarbons**. This means that the alkanes contain hydrogen and carbon only.

All hydrocarbons have a **spine** of **carbon atoms**.

Molecules that belong to the **alkane** family contain **no carbon-to-carbon double bonds**. They are **saturated hydrocarbons**. All the **carbon-to-carbon bonds** in a **saturated** hydrocarbon are **single** bonds. The names of all the members of the alkane family end in **-ane**

The smaller alkanes are gases, but as the molecules increase in size they become liquids and eventually solids. Page 6 of the Data Booklet gives the melting and boiling points of the first eight alkanes.

Top Tip
The names of the first eight alkanes are given in the Data Booklet page 6.

Homologous series

The alkane family make up a **homologous series**. This means that:

- they are all covered by the **same general formula (C_nH_{2n+2})**
- there is a **constant increment** in their formula between one member of the series and the next (CH_2)
- they all have similar chemical properties (take part in the same chemical reactions)
- there is a gradation in their physical properties, such as melting and boiling points.

As the number of carbon atoms increases in the formula then the molecules become bigger in size. The bigger the molecules, the more energy is required to get the molecules to move about rapidly. This explains why the alkanes with the smallest molecules have the lowest boiling points and those with the largest molecules have higher boiling points

CREDIT

Molecular and structural formulae

- The **molecular formula** tells you the **number** of carbon and hydrogen **atoms in each molecule**.
- The **structural formula** shows the **bonds** holding the atoms together. It is simplified so that the molecules look flat, but the atoms are arranged **tetrahedrally.**

The simplest alkane is **methane**. It has molecular formula **CH_4**. This means that every methane molecule contains **one carbon atom and four hydrogen atoms**. The structural formula of methane shows that the carbon atom is **covalently** bonded to each of the four hydrogen atoms.

Formulae of the alkanes

Top Tip
Make sure you know the names, molecular formulae and can draw the structures of these alkanes.

The names, molecular formula and structural formula of the alkanes are shown in the table below. Each carbon atom forms four covalent bonds. Each hydrogen atom can only form one covalent bond.

Name	Molecular formula	Structural formula	Shortened structural formula
Methane	CH_4	H | H–C–H | H	CH_4
Ethane	C_2H_6	H H | | H–C–C–H | | H H	CH_3CH_3
Propane	C_3H_8	H H H | | | H–C–C–C–H | | | H H H	$CH_3CH_2CH_3$
Butane	C_4H_{10}	H H H H | | | | H–C–C–C–C–H | | | | H H H H	$CH_3CH_2CH_2CH_3$
Pentane	C_5H_{12}	H H H H H | | | | | H–C–C–C–C–C–H | | | | | H H H H H	$CH_3CH_2CH_2CH_2CH_3$
Hexane	C_6H_{14}	H H H H H H | | | | | | H–C–C–C–C–C–C–H | | | | | | H H H H H H	$CH_3CH_2CH_2CH_2CH_2CH_3$
Heptane	C_7H_{16}	H H H H H H H | | | | | | | H–C–C–C–C–C–C–C–H | | | | | | | H H H H H H H	$CH_3CH_2CH_2CH_2CH_2CH_2CH_3$
Octane	C_8H_{18}	H H H H H H H H | | | | | | | | H–C–C–C–C–C–C–C–C–H | | | | | | | | H H H H H H H H	$CH_3CH_2CH_2CH_2CH_2CH_2CH_2CH_3$

Quick Test

1. What is meant by a *saturated hydrocarbon*?

2. Write the general formula for the alkane series.

3. What does the molecular formula tell us?

4. Write the molecular formula and draw the structural formula for:
   a) methane
   b) butane.

Answers 1. A hydrocarbon that has no C=C double bonds or one in which all the C–C bonds are single. 2. C_nH_{2n+2} 3. The number of atoms of each element in a molecule. 4. a) CH_4 b) C_4H_{10}

Alkenes

The alkene family

The **alkenes** are another series of **hydrocarbons**. Alkenes also contain hydrogen and carbon only. Like the alkanes, the alkenes have a spine of carbon atoms.

The alkene hydrocarbons contain **carbon-to-carbon double bonds**. They are **unsaturated hydrocarbons** as they contain a double carbon-to-carbon bond. The **names** of all the members of the alkene family end in **-ene**

Alkenes generally have lower melting and boiling points than their equivalent alkanes. The smaller alkenes are gases, but as the molecules increase in size they become liquids and eventually solids. Page 6 in the Data Booklet gives the melting and boiling points of the first five alkenes.

As alkenes must have a double carbon to carbon bond, the simplest alkene must have **two carbon atoms**. The **first member** of the alkene family is called **ethene.** The alkene family also make up a **homologous series**. The general formula for the alkene family is C_nH_{2n}.

Top Tip
The names of the first five alkenes are given in the Data Booklet page 6.

Formulae of the alkenes

Top Tip
Make sure you know the names, molecular formulae and can draw the structures of these alkenes.

The names, molecular formulae and structural formulae of the first five members of the alkene family are shown in the table below.

Name	Molecular formula	Structural formula	Shortened structural formula
Ethene	C_2H_4	H H | | C=C | | H H	$CH_2=CH_2$
Propene	C_3H_6	H H H | | | C=C-C-H | | H H	$CH_2=CHCH_3$
Butene	C_4H_8	H H H H | | | | C=C-C-C-H | | | H H H	$CH_2=CHCH_2CH_3$
Pentene	C_5H_{10}	H H H H H | | | | | C=C-C-C-C-H | | | | H H H H	$CH_2=CHCH_2CH_2CH_3$
Hexene	C_6H_{12}	H H H H H H | | | | | | C=C-C-C-C-C-H | | | | | H H H H H	$CH_2=CHCH_2CH_2CH_2CH_3$

Cracking

Crude oil contains a **mixture** of **hydrocarbons**. The large hydrocarbons separated during the **fractional distillation** of crude oil are not very useful. **Cracking** can break down these large hydrocarbons into **smaller**, **more useful** molecules. There is more demand and therefore a higher price for the smaller hydrocarbons like petrol compared with larger molecules like those in lubricating oil.

Industrial cracking

Cracking is an example of a thermal decomposition reaction. Large, less useful hydrocarbon molecules are broken down into smaller, more useful ones using heat and a hot aluminium oxide catalyst.

The ethene molecule is useful because it contains a double bond between two carbon atoms. Ethene can be used to make plastics and other useful substances.

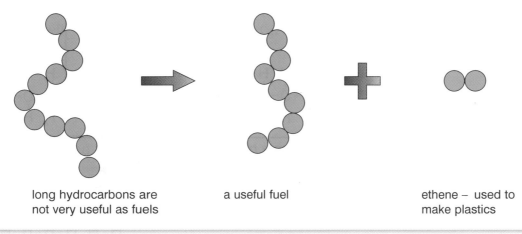

long hydrocarbons are not very useful as fuels   a useful fuel   ethene – used to make plastics

Quick Test

1. What is meant by an *unsaturated hydrocarbon*?

2. Name and draw the structural formula of the first member of the alkene family.

3. What is the general formula for the alkenes?

4. Write down the molecular formula and draw the structural formula for butene.

5. Why are long chain hydrocarbons cracked into smaller ones?

6. Which catalyst is used for cracking?

7. What is ethene used for?

Answers 1. A hydrocarbon which has a carbon to carbon double bond. 2. Ethene

H   H
 \   /
  C=C
 /   \
H   H

3. C_nH_{2n} 4. C_4H_8

H H H   H
| | | |
H-C-C-C=C-H
| | | |
H H H   H

5. To make smaller, more useful hydrocarbons. 6. Aluminium oxide. 7. Making plastics.

Cycloalkanes and isomers

The cycloalkane family

The **cycloalkanes** are another series of **hydrocarbons**. Cycloalkane molecules contain hydrogen and carbon only.

The carbon atoms in cycloalkanes **form a ring** rather than a chain. All the carbon-to-carbon bonds are **single bonds** so the cycloalkanes are **saturated** hydrocarbons. This means that cycloalkanes do not decolourise bromine solution rapidly.

Members of the cycloalkane family make up another **homologous series**. The general formula for the cycloalkane homologous series is C_nH_{2n}.

- The simplest cycloalkane is cyclopropane. It has molecular formula C_3H_6.
- Cyclobutane is the second member of the cycloalkane homologous series. It has molecular formula C_4H_8.

Formulae of the cycloalkanes

The names, molecular formulae and structural formulae of the first four members of the cycloalkane family are shown in the table below.

Name	Molecular formula	Structural formula
Cyclopropane	C_3H_6	
Cyclobutane	C_4H_8	
Cyclopentane	C_5H_{10}	
Cyclohexane	C_6H_{12}	

What are isomers?

Isomers have the same molecular formula but have different structural formulae. For example, butene and cyclobutane are isomers because they both have molecular formula C_4H_8 but their structures are different.

There are two isomers of butane, both with molecular formula C_4H_{10}.

Larger hydrocarbons have more isomers. Pentane has three isomers, hexane has five isomers and heptane has nine isomers.

Top Tip
Make sure you know what isomers are and that you can draw isomers of these hydrocarbons.

Quick Test

1. What is the molecular formula for cyclobutane?

2. What is the general formula for the cycloalkane family?

3. Draw the structural formula for cyclobutane.

4. Which two compounds have molecular formula C_3H_6?

5. What are isomers?

6. Name an isomer of cyclopentane.

7. Draw the structures of the three isomers of pentane.

Answers 1. C_4H_8 2. C_nH_{2n} 3.   4. Propene and cyclopropane. 5. Isomers have the same molecular formula but different structural formulae. 6. Pentene. 7.

Reactions of acids

Acids and metals

When an acid reacts with a metal such as magnesium, **a salt** and **hydrogen gas** are produced (this does not happen with all metals). The hydrogen produced will burn with a squeaky pop.

'squeaky' pop

H₂ gas

burning splint

Mg and H₂SO₄

Hydrogen is produced when an acid reacts with magnesium

Top Tip
Reactions of acids are very important. You should know the formulae for the different acids, the products of these reactions and be able to write formula equations for the reactions.

The word equation for the reaction is:

sulphuric acid + magnesium → magnesium sulphate + hydrogen

The formula equation is:

$H_2SO_4 + Mg \rightarrow MgSO_4 + H_2$

This reaction involves both oxidation and reduction and it is known as a **redox reaction**. The sulphate ions do not change in the reaction. Ions which do not change in a reaction are known as **spectator ions**.

Sulphuric acid contains hydrogen ions, H^+ and sulphate ions, SO_4^{2-}. In the reaction, magnesium metal is reacting with hydrogen ions from the acid. Magnesium atoms are losing electrons to the hydrogen ions. This means that the magnesium atoms are being **oxidised** and the hydrogen ions are being **reduced**.

CREDIT

Acids and alkalis

Alkalis will **neutralise** acids forming a salt and water. The word equation for sodium hydroxide neutralising nitric acid is:

nitric acid + sodium hydroxide → sodium nitrate + water

The formula equation is:

$HNO_3 + NaOH \rightarrow NaNO_3 + H_2O$

CREDIT

In the reaction, the H^+ ions from the acid are reacting with the OH^- ions from the alkali to form water:

$H^+ + OH^- \rightarrow H_2O$

The other ions present are spectator ions.

Acids and metal oxides

Metal oxides will **neutralise** acids to form a salt and water. The word equation for copper(II) oxide reacting with sulphuric acid is:

sulphuric acid + copper(II) oxide → copper(II) sulphate + water

The formula equation is: $H_2SO_4 + CuO \rightarrow CuSO_4 + H_2O$

In the reaction the H^+ ions from the acid are reacting with the O^{2-} ions from the metal oxide to form water:

$2H^+ + O^{2-} \rightarrow H_2O$

The other ions present are spectator ions.

CREDIT

Top Tip
When an acid reacts it is the hydrogen ions from the acid that change. The negative ion in an acid usually behaves as a spectator ion.

Acids and metal carbonates

Metal carbonates will **neutralise** acids to form a salt, water and carbon dioxide. In the reaction, bubbles of carbon dioxide gas will be produced. The carbon dioxide formed turns lime water cloudy.

The word equation for hydrochloric acid reacting with magnesium carbonate is:

hydrochloric acid + magnesium carbonate → magnesium chloride + water + carbon dioxide

The formula equation is:

$HCl + MgCO_3 \rightarrow MgCl_2 + H_2O + CO_2$

CO$_2$ gas

acid and metal carbonate

lime water turns cloudy

Carbon dioxide is produced when a metal carbonate reacts with acid

In the reaction the H^+ ions from the acid are reacting with the CO_3^{2-} ions from the metal carbonate to form water and carbon dioxide:

$2H^+ + CO_3^{2-} \rightarrow H_2O + CO_2$

The other ions present are spectator ions.

CREDIT

Quick Test

1. Which gas is produced when magnesium reacts with hydrochloric acid?

2. Write the balanced formula equation for the reaction of magnesium with hydrochloric acid.

3. Which ion is present in all acid solutions?

4. What are spectator ions?

5. What are the two products when an acid is neutralised by an alkali?

6. What is the test for the gas produced when an acid is neutralised by a metal carbonate?

7. Write down three types of compounds that will neutralise acids.

8. What is the formula for
   a) the oxide ion
   b) the carbonate ion?

Answers 1. Hydrogen gas. **2.** $Mg + 2HCl \rightarrow MgCl_2 + H_2$ **3.** Hydrogen ion, H^+ **4.** Ions which are present but do not change during the reaction. **5.** Salt and water. **6.** The carbon dioxide produced turns lime water cloudy. **7.** Alkalis, metal oxides and metal carbonates. **8. a)** O^{2-} **b)** CO_3^{2-}

Preparation of salts

Insoluble salts

When asked to prepare a salt, it is necessary to find out first if the salt is **soluble** or **insoluble**. This can be done by looking at page 5 of the Data Booklet.

If the salt to be prepared is **insoluble**, then it must be prepared by **precipitation**. This is done by preparing one solution containing the positive ions in the salt and another solution containing the negative ions in the salt. The two solutions are then mixed together to form a precipitate of the salt which is then filtered off.

For example, insoluble lead iodide is made by preparing a solution containing lead ions, such as **lead** nitrate, and another solution containing iodide ions, such as potassium **iodide**. When these two solutions are mixed together a precipitate of **lead iodide** immediately forms:

$$Pb(NO_3)_2(aq) + 2KI(aq) \rightarrow PbI_2(s) + 2KNO_3(aq)$$

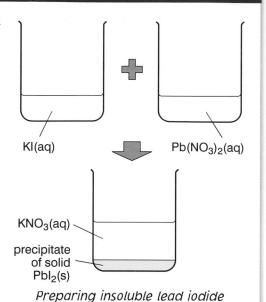

KI(aq)　　Pb(NO$_3$)$_2$(aq)

KNO$_3$(aq)

precipitate of solid PbI$_2$(s)

Preparing insoluble lead iodide

Soluble salts

Soluble salts are prepared from the appropriate acid.

Acid and alkali

The acid and alkali are mixed together until the solution is neutral. This can be checked with pH paper. The water in the salt solution formed is then evaporated off leaving the solid salt behind. This is a good method of preparing sodium and potassium salts.

acid

alkali

pH paper is green showing that neutral salt solution has formed

acid and alkali mixed together

salt solution

HEAT

solid salt

Preparing a soluble salt

Other methods involve reacting the appropriate acid with a solid such as a metal, metal oxide or metal carbonate. The general method is to add excess of the solid to make sure that all the acid has been used up. The solid left over is then filtered off and the salt solution passes through the filter paper. The solid salt is then isolated by evaporating off the water

Acid and metal

Metals can be reacted with acids to form a salt and hydrogen:

metal + acid → salt + hydrogen

zinc + hydrochloric acid → zinc chloride + hydrogen

$$Zn(s) + 2HCl(aq) \rightarrow ZnCl_2(aq) + H_2(g)$$

magnesium + sulphuric acid → magnesium sulphate + hydrogen

$$Mg(s) + H_2SO_4(aq) \rightarrow MgSO_4(aq) \quad + H_2(g)$$

Top Tip
Remember, the solid has to be added in excess to make sure the acid is used up. The excess solid is filtered and the salt solution is heated to evaporate off the water.

Acid and metal oxide

Metal oxides are also bases; they can be reacted with acids to make salts and water:

metal oxide + acid → salt + water

copper oxide + hydrochloric acid → copper chloride + water

$CuO(s)$ + $2HCl(aq)$ → $CuCl_2(aq)$ + $H_2O(l)$

zinc oxide + sulphuric acid → zinc sulphate + water

$ZnO(s)$ + $H_2SO_4(aq)$ → $ZnSO_4(aq)$ + $H_2O(l)$

Acid and metal carbonate

Metal carbonates are also bases; they can be reacted with acids to make salts.

Copper chloride can be made using hydrochloric acid and copper carbonate:

copper carbonate + hydrochloric acid → copper chloride + water + carbon dioxide

$CuCO_3(s)$ + $2HCl(aq)$ → $CuCl_2(aq)$ + $H_2O(l)$ + $CO_2(g)$

- Copper carbonate is added to the acid until it stops fizzing.
- The unreacted copper carbonate is then removed by **filtering**.
- The solution is poured into an evaporating dish.
- It is heated until the first crystals appear.
- The solution is then left for a few days for the copper chloride to **crystallize**.

Top Tip
Sulphuric acid makes sulphate salts. Hydrochloric acid makes chloride salts. Nitric acid makes nitrate salts.

Preparing copper chloride

Quick Test

1. What type of reaction is used to prepare insoluble salts?

2. Which method would be used to prepare sodium nitrate?

3. Which acid and metal would be used to prepare zinc chloride?

4. Which acid and metal oxide would be used to prepare copper sulphate?

5. Which acid and metal carbonate would be used to prepare calcium nitrate?

6. Which method would be used to prepare silver chloride?

Answers 1. Precipitation. **2.** Acid and alkali. **3.** Hydrochloric acid and zinc. **4.** Sulphuric acid and copper oxide. **5.** Nitric acid and calcium carbonate. **6.** Precipitation.

Reactivity of metals

Reactivity series

Some metals are more reactive than others. The **reactivity series** places metals in order of reactivity.

Most reactive

potassium K

sodium Na

calcium Ca

magnesium Mg

zinc Zn

iron Fe

lead Pb

hydrogen H

copper Cu

silver Ag

Least reactive   gold Au

This order has been worked out by observing how vigorous the reaction is between the metal and:

- oxygen
- water
- dilute acid.

Top Tip
The reactivity series is very important. Make sure you know it. The order is very similar to the electrochemical series on page 7 of the Data Booklet.

Reacting metals with oxygen

When metals are heated with air they may react with the oxygen present.

metal   + oxygen → metal oxide

magnesium + oxygen → magnesium oxide

$2Mg(s)$ $+ O_2(g)$ $\rightarrow 2MgO(s)$

Most reactive

potassium K

sodium Na

calcium Ca   These metals react vigorously. They **burn** fiercely.

magnesium Mg

zinc Zn

iron Fe

lead Pb   These metals react **slowly** with air.

hydrogen H

copper Cu

silver Ag   No reaction

Least reactive   gold Au

Reacting metals with water

Some metals react with water to produce a metal hydroxide and hydrogen.

metal + water → metal hydroxide + hydrogen
sodium + water → sodium hydroxide + hydrogen
$2Na(s) + 2H_2O(l) → 2NaOH(aq) + H_2(g)$

Most reactive

potassium K
sodium Na
calcium Ca   React **vigorously** with **cold water**
magnesium Mg
zinc Zn
iron Fe
lead Pb   React very **slowly** with water
hydrogen H
copper Cu
silver Ag   No reaction
gold Au

Least reactive

Top Tip
Remember that potassium and sodium react so violently with water that they must be stored in oil.

Reacting metals with dilute acids

Some metals (those more reactive than hydrogen) react with dilute acids to produce salts and hydrogen.

metal + acid → salt + hydrogen
calcium + hydrochloric acid → calcium chloride + hydrogen
$Ca(s) + 2HCl(aq) → CaCl_2(aq) + H_2(g)$

Most reactive

potassium K
sodium Na
calcium Ca   React **violently** with dilute acid
magnesium Mg
zinc Zn
iron Fe   Reacts **slowly** with dilute acid
lead Pb
hydrogen H
copper Cu
silver Ag   No reaction
gold Au

Least reactive

magnesium   zinc   copper
Putting magnesium, zinc and copper in dilute acid

Quick Test

1. How are very reactive metals extracted from their ores?

2. Which gas do metals react with when they burn in air?

3. What is formed when magnesium burns in air?

4. Write the balanced formula equation for magnesium burning in air.

5. Why does copper not react with hydrochloric acid?

6. Write the balanced formula equation for the reaction between magnesium and hydrochloric acid.

Answers 1. Using electricity (by electrolysis). **2.** oxygen. **3.** Magnesium oxide. **4.** $2Mg + O_2 → 2MgO$ **5.** Copper is below hydrogen in the reactivity series. **6.** $Mg + 2HCl → MgCl_2 + H_2$

Extraction of metals

Metal ores

Only the very unreactive metals such as silver and gold can be found uncombined in the Earth's crust. Most metals are found combined with elements such as oxygen or sulphur in **metal ores.** For example, bauxite is the ore from which aluminium is extracted.

Methods of extraction

The more reactive a metal is, the more difficult it is to extract from its ore.

- The most reactive metals are extracted by **electrolysis** of their molten ores.
- Metals in the middle of the reactivity series are extracted by **heating their ores with carbon or carbon monoxide,**
  e.g. lead oxide + carbon → lead + carbon dioxide.
- The least reactive metals are found **uncombined** in the Earth's crust.

The table below sums this up:

Metal	Method of extraction
Potassium	Electrolysis of molten ore
Sodium	Electrolysis of molten ore
Calcium	Electrolysis of molten ore
Magnesium	Electrolysis of molten ore
Aluminium	Electrolysis of molten ore
Zinc	Heating the ore with carbon or carbon monoxide
Iron	Heating the ore with carbon or carbon monoxide
Tin	Heating the ore with carbon or carbon monoxide
Lead	Heating the ore with carbon or carbon monoxide
Copper	Heating the ore with carbon or carbon monoxide
Silver	Metal occurs uncombined
Gold	Metal occurs uncombined

Top Tip
The more reactive the metal, the more difficult it is to extract from its ore.

Extraction of iron: the blast furnace

The main ore of iron is iron oxide or haematite Fe_2O_3. Iron is extracted from iron oxide by **reduction** (removal of oxygen) in the blast furnace.

The solid raw materials added to the blast furnace are:

* iron ore (haematite)
* coke (almost pure carbon)
* limestone (reacts with impurities).

What happens in the blast furnace

1. Hot air enters the blast furnace and reacts with carbon, forming carbon dioxide and releasing energy.

   carbon + oxygen → carbon dioxide

   $C(s)$ + $O_2(g)$ → $CO_2(g)$

2. At high temperatures the carbon dioxide reacts with more carbon to form carbon monoxide.

   carbon dioxide + carbon → carbon monoxide

   $CO_2(g)$ + $C(s)$ → $2CO(g)$

3. The carbon monoxide reduces the iron oxide to iron.

   carbon monoxide + iron oxide → iron + carbon dioxide

   $3CO(g)$ + $Fe_2O_3(s)$ → $2Fe(l)$ + $3CO_2(g)$

The iron is dense (heavy) and sinks to the bottom, where it is tapped off.

Removal of impurities

Haematite may contain **impurities**, most commonly **silicon dioxide** (silica). When **limestone** is added it removes the silica by forming molten **slag**. The slag has a low density so floats on the top of the molten iron ore. The slag can be used in road building.

Top Tip
Remember that the blast furnace is used to extract iron from iron ore.

three solids are added:
iron ore
coke
limestone

VERY HOT

slag (limestone impurities) is found on top of the iron

hot air blasted into furnace

molten or liquid iron is found at the bottom

The blast furnace

Quick Test

1. Which elements are so unreactive it can be found uncombined?

2. What method of extraction should be used for zinc and lead?

3. What method of extraction should be used for the most reactive metals?

4. What is the name and formula of the main iron ore?

5. What three solid raw materials are added to the blast furnace?

6. Which other reactant is blasted into the furnace?

7. Which gas actually reduces the iron oxide?

8. Why does the iron sink to the bottom?

9. What substance is formed when limestone reacts with silica?

10. What can this substance be used for?

Answers 1. Gold and silver **2.** Heating with carbon **3.** Electrolysis **4.** Haematite, Fe_2O_3 **5.** Iron ore, coke, limestone **6.** Hot air **7.** Carbon monoxide **8.** It is more dense. **9.** Slag **10.** Road building

Introducing plastics and synthetic fibres

Natural and synthetic materials

Materials can be classified as **natural or synthetic**.

Natural materials come from **plants and animals** and include:

- wool from sheep
- wood from trees
- leather from animal skins
- cotton from plants
- rubber from plants.

Synthetic materials are made in factories. Many plastics and synthetic fibres are made from **oil**.

- The first process in the refinery is **fractional distillation**. This separates crude oil into fractions according to their boiling points.
- The second process is **cracking**. This breaks the long chain hydrocarbons into the more desirable smaller chain hydrocarbons. The cracking process also produces small unsaturated molecules such as ethene which are used to make plastics.

Top Tip
Make sure you know the differences between natural and synthetic materials.

Advantages and disadvantages of natural and synthetic materials

An advantage that natural materials have over synthetic materials is that natural materials are **biodegradable.** This means that they are attacked by bacteria and rot away when they are discarded. Synthetic plastics are not usually biodegradable and their durability causes litter and environmental problems when they are discarded.

Synthetic materials have an advantage in that they can be tailored to fit the required property. However, synthetic plastics may burn to produce toxic fumes. If the plastic contains chlorine, toxic hydrogen chloride may be produced. Polyurethane plastics may produce very poisonous hydrogen cyanide if they are burning or smouldering. If plastics are burned in a limited supply of oxygen, carbon monoxide may be formed.

Top Tip
Make sure you know what biodegradable means.

Thermoplastics and thermosetting plastics

- A **thermoplastic** softens on heating and can be remoulded or reshaped more than once. Examples include **polythene, polystyrene, polyvinylchloride** and other addition polymers.

- A **thermosetting plastic** does not soften on heating and cannot be reshaped. Examples include **bakelite** and **urea-methanal**. Since they are unaffected by heating, thermosetting plastics are used in electric plugs and sockets. Melamine is a thermosetting plastic which is used to make kitchen surfaces as it will not melt when hot pans are placed on it.

Examples of thermosetting plastics

Uses of plastics

Poly(ethene)

- Poly(ethene) is **cheap** and **strong**.
- It is used for plastic **bags** and **bottles**.

Poly(propene)

- Poly(propene) is **strong** and has a high **elasticity**.
- It is used for **crates** and **ropes**.

Poly(chloroethene), PVC

- PVC is **rigid** and is used for building materials such as **drain pipes**.
- With plasticisers added, it is used for **wellingtons** and **mackintoshes**.
- PVC is also used as insulation around electrical wires and cables.

Poly(styrene)

- Poly(styrene) is **cheap** and can be **moulded** into different shapes.
- It is used for **packaging** and for plastic **casings**.

Quick Test

1. What does synthetic mean?
2. Where do most synthetic materials come from?
3. What does biodegradable mean?
4. Write down two disadvantages of synthetic plastics.
5. What is meant by thermosetting?
6. Name two thermoplastics.
7. Write down a property and use for poly(propene).

Answers 1. Artificial or man-made. **2.** Crude oil. **3.** Attacked by bacteria and rots away naturally. **4.** They cause environmental problems since they are not biodegradable: they may burn to produce toxic fumes. **5.** Does not soften on heating. **6.** Poly(ethene), poly(styrene), poly(propene), etc. **7.** Strong and elastic, used for crates and ropes.

Fertilisers

The need for fertilisers

Increasing world population means that fertilisers are needed to make food production more efficient.

Plant growth involves a series of complicated chemical reactions. Growing plants need **nutrients** and different crops need fertilisers containing the elements **nitrogen (N), phosphorus (P) and potassium (K)** in different proportions.

Which compounds are in fertilisers?

Fertilisers can be natural or artificial. Natural fertilisers include manure and compost.

When plants are growing they are removing nutrients from the soil. Adding fertilisers restores essential elements back into the soil. The main elements needed by plants are nitrogen, phosphorus and potassium. Because plants take up nutrients through their roots, fertilisers need to be soluble in water. Useful synthetic fertilisers include:

a compost bin

- ammonium salts; contain N
- nitrate salts; contain N
- phosphate salts; contain P
- potassium salts; contain K.

Top Tip
Remember NPK; the essential elements in fertilisers.

Page 5 of the Data Booklet shows that ammonium compounds and nitrate compounds are very soluble, so these make good fertilisers. Potassium compounds are also very soluble. The element phosphorus is present in phosphate compounds. Phosphates are not so soluble but ammonium phosphate and potassium phosphate are soluble. Synthetic fertilisers contain mixtures of different compounds containing these essential elements. Different plants need these essential elements in different proportions.

Problems with fertilisers

In areas of high rainfall, some of the artificial fertilisers added to the soil may be washed away by rainwater and end up in lochs and rivers. Here the nitrates encourage bacteria and algae to grow, and this uses up the dissolved oxygen in the water. Fish and other animals therefore cannot get enough oxygen and die.

Urea is only slightly soluble and is a useful fertiliser in areas of high rainfall.

Changing free nitrogen into fixed nitrogen

Nitrogen gas is known as **free nitrogen**. When nitrogen is combined with other elements in compounds it is known as **fixed nitrogen**. Almost 80 per cent of the air is nitrogen gas. Nitrogen is an unreactive gas and will react only under extreme conditions where a lot of energy is supplied by a high voltage spark. Nitrogen and oxygen in the air react together to form nitrogen dioxide, NO_2, during lightning storms.

Certain plants such as peas, beans and clover contain **nitrogen-fixing bacteria** in nodules on their roots.

These bacteria can change nitrogen from the air (free nitrogen) into nitrogen compounds (fixed nitrogen) at ordinary temperatures. The plants can then absorb these nitrogen compounds and convert them into proteins. Peas, beans and clover are good for the soil as they make it more fertile and this is cheaper than using chemical fertilisers.

Top Tip
Remember peas, beans and clover can convert free nitrogen into fixed nitrogen.

The nitrogen cycle

The nitrogen cycle shows how nitrogen is recycled between plants, animals and the air. The decomposition of plant and animal protein is very important in the recycling of nitrogen, and this is a major part of the natural nitrogen cycle. To maintain soil fertility and to feed the increasing world population, artificial fertiliser must be added to the nitrogen cycle. A simplified nitrogen cycle is shown on the right.

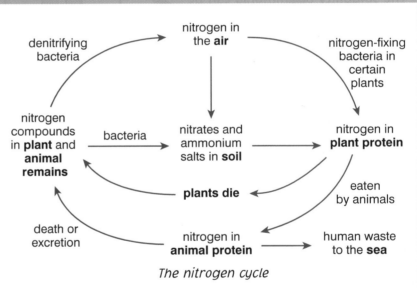

The nitrogen cycle

Quick Test

1. Name a plant that has nitrogen-fixing bacteria in nodules on its roots.
2. Give three reasons why potassium nitrate is useful as a fertiliser.
3. What will happen to algae living in a loch if nitrates are present in the water?
4. Why are fertilisers needed?
5. Which three elements are the main nutrients needed by growing plants?
6. What is the difference between free nitrogen and fixed nitrogen?

Carbohydrates

What are carbohydrates?

The word **carbo-hydr-ate** tells us that the elements **carbon, hydrogen and oxygen** must be present. The experiment shown right demonstrates that carbohydrates contain carbon and water.

The hydrogen and oxygen in carbohydrates are in the ratio 2:1, just as they are in water.

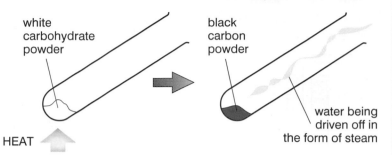

white carbohydrate powder

HEAT

black carbon powder

water being driven off in the form of steam

Heating carbohydrate to produce carbon and water

Names and formulae of carbohydrates

The table right gives the names and formulae of common carbohydrates.

Starch is a **polymer** made from many glucose molecules joined together. When two glucose molecules join together, water is lost:

Name of carbohydrate	Formula
Glucose	$C_6H_{12}O_6$
Fructose	$C_6H_{12}O_6$
Sucrose	$C_{12}H_{22}O_{11}$
Maltose	$C_{12}H_{22}O_{11}$
Starch	$(C_6H_{10}O_5)n$

Top Tip

Carbohydrates with the formula $C_6H_{12}O_6$ are monosaccharides, e.g. glucose. Carbohydrates with the formula $C_{12}H_{22}O_{11}$ are disaccharides, e.g. sucrose. Starch is a polysaccharide.

$$C_6H_{12}O_6 + C_6H_{12}O_6 \rightarrow C_{12}H_{22}O_{11} + H_2O$$

When many glucose molecules join together, each glucose molecule that joins loses a water molecule. That is why the formula for starch is given as $(C_6H_{10}O_5)_n$ (since $C_6H_{12}O_6 - H_2O = C_6H_{10}O_5$). This type of polymerisation, where small molecules join together to make a large molecule and water, is known as **condensation polymerisation**.

Glucose and fructose have the same molecular formula but their structures are different and so glucose and fructose are **isomers**. (Isomers have the same molecular formula but different structures.) Maltose and sucrose are also isomers.

Solubility of carbohydrates

Most carbohydrates such as glucose and sucrose dissolve easily in water to form sweet tasting solutions. These carbohydrates are sometimes called **sugars** and are often added to foods and drinks.

Starch does not taste sweet and does not dissolve in water to form a true solution. If a light beam is shone through a test tube of glucose solution and a test tube containing starch in water, the light beam does not show up in the glucose solution but shows up in the other test tube as the light reflects off the starch molecules. This shows that starch molecules are bigger than glucose molecules.

Tests on carbohydrates

Test for starch

Starch turns **iodine solution** a **blue-black** colour. No other carbohydrate does this so this test can be used to distinguish starch from other carbohydrates.

brown iodine solution being added to starch

blue-black colour appears

Starch turns iodine blue-black

Test for glucose

Benedict's (or Fehling's) solution can be used to test for **glucose**. **Blue** Benedict's or Fehling's solution turns **orange-brown** in glucose solution when heated in a hot water bath.

Top Tip
The two tests on this page are important. Make sure you know how to carry them out and what the results mean.

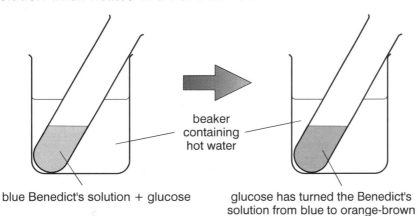

beaker containing hot water

blue Benedict's solution + glucose

glucose has turned the Benedict's solution from blue to orange-brown

Glucose turns Benedict's solution orange-brown

If you were given unlabelled samples of glucose, sucrose and starch, these tests would enable you to tell which was which. Remember, iodine is used to test for starch, Benedict's solution can be used to test for glucose, but there is no test for sucrose

CREDIT

Benedict's solution will react with some other carbohydrates in the same way as it reacts with glucose. These carbohydrates include fructose, maltose and lactose, and carbohydrates which react in this way with Benedict's solution are known as **reducing sugars**.

Quick Test

1. Which elements are present in carbohydrates?

2. Which experiment shows that starch molecules are bigger than glucose molecules?

3. What is the chemical test for starch?

4. How would you distinguish experimentally between glucose and sucrose?

5. Write down the molecular formula for:
   a) glucose
   b) sucrose.

Answers 1. Carbon, hydrogen and oxygen. **2.** The light beam experiment. **3.** Starch will turn iodine solution blue-black. **4.** Use Benedict's solution: glucose will turn blue Benedict's solution orange. Sucrose will have no effect. **5. a)** $C_6H_{12}O_6$ **b)** $C_{12}H_{22}O_{11}$

Breaking down carbohydrates

Structure of carbohydrates

The molecular structure of carbohydrates is very complex. Glucose and fructose both have the molecular formula $C_6H_{12}O_6$. We can represent the structure of these monosaccharides as:

HO—⬡G—OH   and   HO—⬡F—OH

We can represent three glucose molecules joining together to form part of a starch polymer molecule as:

HO—⬡G—OH + HO—⬡G—OH + HO—⬡G—OH   3 glucose molecules

⟶   —O—⬡G—O—⬡G—O—⬡G—O—   part of a starch molecule containing 3 glucose molecules joined together

+ H_2O + H_2O + H_2O

Similarly, sucrose (a disaccharide containing one glucose molecule and one fructose molecule joined together) can be represented as:

HO—⬡G—O—⬡F—OH

Digestion of sucrose

When sucrose (ordinary table sugar) is eaten it is **digested** (broken down) in our body into glucose and fructose:

HO—⬡G—O—⬡F—OH   ⟶   HO—⬡G—OH + HO—⬡F—OH
+ H_2O

When sucrose is made in plants, one glucose molecule and one fructose molecule join together by **condensation**. It is known as condensation because water molecules are also formed in the reaction.

Breaking down or digesting sucrose takes place in the presence of water. The H from the water molecule joins onto one of the products and the OH from the water molecule joins onto the other product. This is an example of **hydrolysis**. Hydrolysis is the reverse of condensation just as respiration is the reverse of photosynthesis. Hydrolysis is the breaking down of a large molecule into smaller molecules using water.

The chemical reactions taking place in our digestive system are all hydrolysis reactions. They usually take place in the presence of acid or **enzymes** which speed up the hydrolysis reactions. Enzymes are **biological catalysts**. They speed up reactions in living things such as plants and animals.

Top Tip
Remember the reactions, condensation and hydrolysis, and that one is the reverse of the other.

Digestion of starch

When we digest foods such as bread and potatoes that contain large amounts of starch, the starch molecules are broken down into smaller glucose molecules. Starch molecules are too big to travel through the gut wall into the bloodstream. The smaller glucose molecules can pass through the gut wall into the bloodstream where they can be transported around the body.

In the laboratory, starch can be broken down into smaller molecules using either dilute acid or the enzyme amylase. Enzymes such as amylase act as biological catalysts. This means that they speed up chemical reactions in living things such as plants and animals. In our digestive system, enzymes help to break down the complex molecules present in the food we eat into smaller more useful molecules.

The diagram below shows part of the starch polymer molecule breaking into three glucose molecules.

Top Tip
Remember that starch is made from many glucose molecules joined together.

part of a starch molecule containing 3 glucose molecules joined together

$$-O-G-O-G-O-G-O-$$
$$+ H_2O \quad + H_2O \quad + H_2O$$

$$\rightarrow HO-G-OH + HO-G-OH + HO-G-OH$$

3 glucose molecules

At the beginning of the above reaction the starch will turn iodine solution a blue-black colour. After some time the starch will no longer react with the iodine solution because its large molecules are breaking down. When this happens the reaction mixture can be tested with Benedict's solution. This will change colour from blue to orange-brown, showing that glucose is made when starch breaks down.

Quick Test

1. Draw a diagram to show two glucose molecules joined together.

2. What type of chemical reaction is occurring when glucose molecules join together to form a disaccharide?

3. What name is given to the chemical reaction in which starch is broken down into glucose?

4. What is an enzyme?

5. Which enzyme is involved in the digestion of starch in our bodies?

Answers 1. HO-G-O-G-OH **2.** Condensation. **3.** Hydrolysis **4.** A biological catalyst. **5.** Amylase.

Fermentation

What happens during fermentation?

Fermentation is the chemical reaction in which **glucose** breaks down to form **alcohol** and **carbon dioxide**. The enzyme, **zymase**, produced by **yeast** is the **catalyst** for the reaction.

The equation for the fermentation reaction is:

$$C_6H_{12}O_6 \rightarrow 2C_2H_5OH + 2CO_2$$

Ethanol is the alcohol found in alcoholic drinks.

A fermentation experiment that can be done in the laboratory is shown below:

a fermentation reaction

Top Tip
Enzymes are affected by changes in pH and temperature.
• Most enzymes work best at a temperature between 25°C and 40°C.
• Most enzymes in the human body work best at pH7.

Alcohol and alcoholic drinks

Alcoholic drinks are made by fermentation. Alcohols are poisonous and the least poisonous alcohol, ethanol, is the one present in alcoholic drinks. Ethanol is the second member of the alkanol family. It has the formula C_2H_5OH and its full structural formula is:

$$H-\overset{\displaystyle \overset{H}{|}}{\underset{\displaystyle \underset{H}{|}}{C}}-\overset{\displaystyle \overset{H}{|}}{\underset{\displaystyle \underset{H}{|}}{C}}-OH$$

Top Tip
Ethanol is the only alcohol that you need to know. You should be able to write its chemical formula and full structural formula.

Alcoholic drinks have been made for over one thousand years. One of the reasons that there are so many different types of alcoholic drinks is that the glucose for the fermentation can come from different plant sources. Alcoholic drinks can be made from any fruit or vegetable that contains starch or sugars. The table below gives some examples.

Alcoholic drink	Plant used	Approximate % of alcohol
Beer	Barley	4
Wine	Grapes	13
Cider	Apples	5
Sherry	Grapes	20
Whisky	Barley	40

Distillation

When the concentration of alcohol in the fermenting mixture reaches about 10 per cent, the yeasts are killed and the fermentation reaction stops so no more alcohol will form.

Drinks with an alcohol content much above 10 per cent must be **distilled** after fermentation has taken place. These drinks include whisky, brandy, gin and vodka. These alcoholic drinks are usually known as spirits.

Distillation is **evaporation** followed by **condensation**. It is used to separate the alcohol from the aqueous mixture (the alcohol has boiling point 79 °C compared to the boiling point of water which is 100 °C).

During distillation the fermented mixture is warmed gently. When the temperature reaches 79 °C, the ethanol will boil off. The temperature will remain at 79 °C until almost all the ethanol has been removed. If the temperature is allowed to rise to 100 °C then the water will evaporate off.

The apparatus used in the laboratory for distillation is shown below.

apparatus required for distillation

Quick Test

1. What are the two products formed during the fermentation of glucose?

2. Draw the full structural formula of ethanol.

3. Which technique is used to separate alcohol from water and why does it work?

Calculations 1

Please note that the calculations in this chapter are all at credit level in Standard Grade Chemistry.

Number of protons, electrons and neutrons in ions

This subject has been touched on in an earlier chapter but here it is done in slightly more detail.

Atomic number and mass number

Two important quantities are the **atomic number** and the **mass number**.

The atomic number is the number of protons in an atom. Atoms are **neutral** overall because they have **equal numbers** of **positive protons** in the nucleus and **negative electrons** outside the nucleus. However atoms can lose and gain electrons to form **ions**.

Atoms of **metal elements** tend to lose electrons to form **positive ions**. Atoms of **non-metal elements** tend to gain electrons to form **negative ions**. **The mass number is the sum of the protons and neutrons in an atom.**

So, if we are given the nuclide notation of atoms and ions, we can work out the number of protons, neutrons and electrons as in the examples below.

> **Top Tip**
> Make sure you understand the distinction between atoms and ions.

Example

Calculate the number of protons, neutrons and electrons in $^{35}Cl^-$.

- All chlorine atoms and ions have an atomic number of 17, **so the number of protons must be 17**.

- The chloride ion, Cl^-, has a charge of −1 and so has one extra electron compared to a chlorine atom. This means that the number of electrons is one more than the number of protons. So **the number of electrons is 18**.

- The number of neutrons is found by subtracting the atomic number from the mass number. So **the number of neutrons = 35 − 17 = 18**.

Example

Calculate the number of protons, neutrons and electrons in $^{25}Mg^{2+}$

- All magnesium atoms and ions have an atomic number of 12, **so the number of protons must be 12**.

- The magnesium ion, Mg^{2+}, has a charge of +2 so it has two fewer electrons than a magnesium atom. So the number of electrons is two fewer than the number of protons. So **the number of electrons is 10**.

- The number of neutrons is found by subtracting the atomic number from the mass number. So **the number of neutrons = 25 − 12 = 13**.

Relative atomic mass

The **relative atomic mass (RAM)** is used to **compare** the masses of different atoms. The **relative atomic mass** of an element is the average mass of its isotopes compared with an atom of $^{12}_{6}C$.

$^{4}_{2}He$ — mass number / atomic number (or proton number)

RAM of helium = 4

$^{24}_{12}Mg$

RAM of magnesium = 24

Most elements exist as a mixture of different isotopes and the relative atomic mass is the average atomic mass. Therefore the relative atomic mass is rarely a whole number. The approximate relative atomic masses are given in the Data Booklet on page 4 and have been rounded to the nearest 0.5

Top Tip
Remember that the relative atomic masses of most elements are given in the Data Booklet. Mass numbers are **not** given in the Data Booklet and these should not be confused with relative atomic masses.

Formula mass

The **formula mass** of any molecule is worked out by adding together the **atomic masses** of all the atoms in the molecule.

- For carbon dioxide, CO_2:

The formula mass of CO_2 is **44**.

$C O_2$
$12 + (2 \times 16) = 44$

- For water, H_2O:

The formula mass of H_2O is **18**.

$H_2 O$
$(2 \times 1) + 16 = 18$

- For ammonia, NH_3:

The formula mass of NH_3 is **17**.

$N H_3$
$14 + (3 \times 1) = 17$

Top Tip
Remember that the relative atomic masses of the more common elements are given in the table on page 4 of the Data Booklet.

The mole

No units are given for formula masses.

Very often in chemistry we need to know actual quantities. To do this we use a value known as **the mole**.

The mole is the gram formula mass of a substance. This is really the same as the formula mass, but with grams as the unit.

Examples

Using the same examples as above:
- 1 mole of carbon dioxide, CO_2, is 44g and 1 mole of water, H_2O, is 18g.
- 2 moles of ammonia will be $2 \times 17g = 34g$ and 0.5 moles of water will be $18 \times 0.5 = 9g$.

Quick Test

1. How many protons, neutrons and electrons are in:
   a. $^{18}O^{2-}$. b. $^{24}Na^+$. c. $^{27}Al^{3+}$. d. $^{79}Br^-$

2. When calculated accurately, why is the relative atomic mass for most elements not a whole number?

3. Calculate the formula mass for:
   a. CO.   b. NaOH.
   c. magnesium oxide.   d. calcium carbonate

4. Calculate the mass of 2 moles of:
   a. NaOH.   b. magnesium oxide.
   c. calcium carbonate.   d. sodium chloride.

Answers 1. a. 8 p, 10 n, 10 e. **b.** 11 p, 13 n, 10 e. **c.** 13 p, 14 n, 10 e. **d.** 35 p, 44 n, 36 e. **2.** Because it is an average mass of the different isotopes of the element. **3 a.** 28. **b.** 40. **c.** 40.5. **d.** 100. **4. a.** 80g. **b.** 91g. **c.** 200g. **d.** 117g.

Calculations 2

Moles to mass and mass to moles

To do some calculations it is helpful to know and use the triangle below. This shows the relationship between the number of moles, n, the mass and formula mass, FM, of a substance.

n = number of moles
FM = formula mass

Using this formula
$n = Mass/FM$
$Mass = n \times FM$
$FM = mass/n$

Examples

Question 1:   Calculate the number of moles in 10 g of sodium hydroxide.

Worked answer: Sodium hydroxide has formula NaOH
Formula Mass, FM, of NaOH = 23 + 16 + 1 = 40
Mass = 10g
n = mass/FM = 10/40 = **0.25 moles**

Question 2:   Calculate the mass of 2 moles of calcium chloride.

Worked answer: Calcium chloride has formula $CaCl_2$
Formula mass, FM, of $CaCl_2$ = 40 + (35.5 × 2) = 111
Number of moles, n = 2
Mass = n × FM = 2 × 111 = **222g**

Concentrations of a solution

The concentration of a solution is the **quantity of solute dissolved in a certain volume of solution**.

In chemistry, the concentration is **measured in units of moles per litre (mol/l)**.
For example:
1 mole of sodium hydroxide, NaOH, has a mass of 40.0 g.
So 1 litre of 1mol/l NaOH(aq) will contain 40.0 g of sodium hydroxide in 1 litre of solution.

Another triangle, which is useful in calculations involving volume and concentration of solutions, such as dilute acids and alkalis, is shown below.

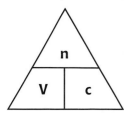

n = number of moles
V = volume of solution (**in litres**)
c = concentration of solution (**in mol/l**)

Using this triangle,
$n = V \times c$
$c = n/V$

Example

Question 1:   Calculate the number of moles in 500 cm³ of a 0.2 mol/l solution.

Worked answer: The volume, V, is 500 cm³ = **0.5 litres**
The concentration, c = **0.2 mol/l**
n = V × c = **0.5 × 0.2 = 0.1 moles**

Calculations using both formulae

Sometimes, in more difficult calculations, it is necessary to use both triangles.

Examples

When preparing solutions of a certain concentration, it is necessary to work out how much of the solute is needed.

Question 1: Calculate the mass of sodium hydroxide required to prepare $250\,cm^3$ of a solution of concentration $0.1\,mol/l$.

Worked answer: In this calculation we are told:
- the volume, $V = 250\,cm^3$ which is 0.25 litres and
- the concentration, $c = 0.1\,mol/l$

We can **calculate the number of moles** using the formula

$n = V \times c = 0.25 \times 0.1 =$ **0.025 moles**

The formula of sodium hydroxide is NaOH, so the formula mass can be calculated as:

$FM = 23 + 16 + 1 = 40$.

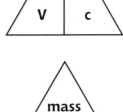

To calculate the **mass** we have to use the other formula

$Mass = n \times FM = 0.025 \times 40 =$ **1.0 g**

So the mass of sodium hydroxide required is 1.0 g

Question 2. What will be the concentration of $500\,cm^3$ of solution containing 50.0 g of sodium hydroxide?

Worked answer: In this calculation we are told:
- the volume, $V = 500\,cm^3$ which is 0.50 litres and
- the mass which is 50.0 g of NaOH.

We can work out the formula mass of NaOH to be 40.0, so we can work out the number of moles of NaOH using this triangle.

The number of moles, $n = mass/FM = 50.0/40.0 =$ **1.25 moles**

The concentration can now be calculated using the other triangle.

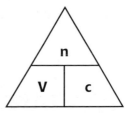

$c = n / V = 1.25 / 0.5 =$ **2.5 mol/l**

So the concentration of the sodium hydroxide solution will be 2.5 mol/l.

Calculations 3

Calculations from results of titrations

This type of calculation is used to find out the concentration of an acid or alkali after having done a **titration**.

A titration experiment involves using a burette, which is used to dispense accurately measured volumes of a liquid - usually, the acid solution. The acid from the burette flows into a conical flask which would normally contain a known volume of the alkali plus a few drops of indicator. The indicator changes colour when the neutralisation reaction is complete.

If the volumes of both the acid and alkali are known and the concentration of one of them also known, then the concentration of the other can be calculated.

To do this we can use the formula:

$$P_{acid} \times V_{acid} \times c_{acid} = P_{alkali} \times V_{alkali} \times c_{alkali}$$

Where: P = power
        V = volume
        c = concentration

burette

acid solution, e.g. dilute hydrochloric acid HCl(aq)

white tile

alkali solution, e.g. sodium hydroxide NaOH(aq) + indicator

- **The power of an acid is the number of H^+ ions in the formula**
  (e.g. hydrochloric acid HCl has a power of 1; sulphuric acid H_2SO_4 has a power of 2).

- **The power of an alkali is the number of OH^- ions in the formula**
  (e.g. sodium hydroxide NaOH has a power of 1; calcium hydroxide $Ca(OH)_2$ has a power of 2).

Example

Question.   In a titration experiment, $16.2\,cm^3$ of $0.1\,mol/l$ sulphuric acid was needed to neutralise $25.0\,cm^3$ of sodium hydroxide solution. Calculate the concentration of the sodium hydroxide solution.

Worked Answer: H_2SO_4 has power = 2, so $P_{acid} = 2$
            The volume of the acid is $16.2\ cm^3$, so $V_{acid} = 16.2$
            The acid has concentration $0.1\ mol/l$ so $c_{acid} = 0.1$

            NaOH has power = 1, so $P_{alkali} = 1$
            The volume of the alkali is $25.0\ cm^3$, so $V_{alkali} = 25.0$
            The unknown is c_{alkali}

$$P_{acid} \times V_{acid} \times c_{acid} = P_{alkali} \times V_{alkali} \times c_{alkali}$$

$$2 \times 16.2 \times 0.1 = 1 \times 25.0 \times c_{alkali}$$

$$\text{So } c_{alkali} = \frac{2 \times 16.2 \times 0.1}{1 \times 25.0}$$

$$= 0.13\ mol/l$$

So the concentration of the sodium hydroxide was 0.13 mol/l

- Calculations from the results of titrations are used to find out the concentration of an acid or alkali.
- If the volumes of both the acid and the alkali are known, and the concentration of one of them known, then the concentration of the other can be calculated from the results of the titration experiment.

Quick Test

1. Calculate the number of moles in
   a. 9 g of H_2O
   b. 11.7 g of NaCl
   c. 1.0 g of $CaCO_3$

2. Calculate the number of moles in
   a. 12.7 g of iodine
   b. 8.8 g of carbon dioxide
   c. 2.6 g of calcium fluoride

3. Calculate the mass of
   a. 0.1 moles of CO
   b. 3 moles of $CuSO_4$
   c. 0.02 moles of calcium chloride
   d. 3.1 moles of carbon

4. Calculate the number of moles in
   a. 100 cm³ of 0.1 mol/l solution
   b. 50 cm³ of 0.25 mol/l solution
   c. 250 cm³ of 2.0 mol/l solution
   d. 500 cm³ of 0.01 mol/l solution

5. Calculate the mass of sodium hydroxide required to prepare
   a. 100 cm³ of 2 mol/l solution
   b. 2 litres of 0.012 mol/l solution
   c. 50 cm³ of 0.2 mol/l solution
   d. 250 cm³ of 0.3 mol/l solution

6. Calculate the mass of sodium nitrate required to prepare
   a. 100 cm³ of 0.2 mol/l solution
   b. 2 litres of 0.01 mol/l solution
   c. 50 cm³ of 0.2 mol/l solution
   d. 250 cm³ of 0.1 mol/l solution

7. What will be the concentration of 200 cm³ of a solution containing
   a. 2.4 g of LiOH?
   b. 0.8 g of NaOH?
   c. 1 g of calcium hydroxide?
   d. 0.17 g of silver(I) nitrate?

8. In a titration, 25.0 cm³ of 0.10 mol/l NaOH was exactly neutralised by 22.2 cm³ of hydrochloric acid. Calculate the concentration of the hydrochloric acid.

9. What volume of 0.2 mol/l sulphuric acid will exactly neutralise 25.0 cm³ of 0.5 mol/l potassium hydroxide?

Answers 1. a. 0.5 moles **b.** 0.2 moles **c.** 0.01 moles **2. a.** 0.05 moles **b.** 0.2 moles **c.** 0.033 moles **3. a.** 2.8g **b.** 478.5g **c.** 2.22g **d.** 37.2g **4. a.** 0.01 moles **b.** 0.0125 moles **c.** 0.5 moles **d.** 0.005 moles **5. a.** 8.0g **b.** 0.96g **c.** 0.40g **d.** 3.0g **6. a.** 1.7g **b.** 1.7g **c.** 0.85g **d.** 2.125g **7. a.** 0.5 mol/l **b.** 0.1 mol/l **c.** 0.068 mol/l **d.** 0.005 mol/l **8.** 0.11 mol/l **9.** 31.25 cm³

Calculations 4 CREDIT

Empirical formula calculations

The **empirical formula** of a compound gives **the simplest ratio of the atoms present** in that compound.

For example, ethane has molecular formula C_2H_6.

- This means that in one molecule of ethane there are two carbon atoms and six hydrogen atoms.
- The ratio of carbon atoms to hydrogen atoms is 2:6 and so the simplest ratio is 1:3
- So, the empirical formula will be CH_3.

The empirical formula is obtained by calculating the simplest ratio using the results of an experiment.

Example

An experiment to determine the empirical formula of copper oxide is shown right:

A set of experimental results is:

- Mass of test tube   = 49.43 g
- Mass of test tube + copper oxide at start   = 51.42 g
- So mass of copper oxide = 51.42 – 49.43   = 1.99 g
- Mass of test tube + copper at the end   = 51.02 g
- So mass of copper = 51.02 – 49.43   = 1.59 g
- Mass of oxygen in the copper oxide = 1.99 – 159 = 0.40 g

To get the empirical formula we must first calculate the number of moles of each element using the formula, n = mass/FM

$n_{for\ Cu}$ = 1.59/63.5 = 0.025 moles of Cu $n_{for\ O}$ = 0.40/16 = 0.025 moles of O

Since there are equal numbers of moles of Cu and O, then the empirical formula is **CuO**.

Example

This is a more difficult example.

Question.   Calculate the empirical formula of a compound containing 1.84 g of sodium, 1.28 g of sulphur and 2.56 g of oxygen.

Worked Answer: Sometimes it is easier to set out empirical formula calculations in a table as shown below.

Element	Na	S	O
Mass/g	1.84	1.28	2.56
Number of moles (= mass/FM)	1.84/23	1.28/32	2.56/16
	0.08	0.04	0.16
Divide by the smallest number (to get the whole number ratio)	0.08/0.04 = 2	0.04/0.04 = 1	0.16/0.16 = 4

So the empirical formula is $Na_2S_1O_4$ or simply, Na_2SO_4

Percentage composition

Percentage mass of an element in a compound $= \dfrac{\text{atomic mass} \times \text{no. of atoms}}{\text{formula mass}} \times 100\%$

Example

Ammonium nitrate, NH_4NO_3, is used as a fertiliser.
Find the percentage composition of nitrogen in this compound.

- RAM of N = 14
- RAM of H = 1
- RAM of O = 16

The formula mass of NH_4NO_3 is:

- $14 + (4 \times 1) + 14 + (3 \times 16) = 80$

Percentage of nitrogen $= \dfrac{14 \times 2}{80} \times 100\% = 35\%$

- **Ammonium nitrate is 35% nitrogen**

Key Fact

1 The empirical formula of a compound gives the simplest ratio of the atoms present in that compound.
2 Obtain the empirical formula by calculating the simplest ratio using the results of an experiment.

Quick Test

1. Calculate the empirical formula of the compound which contains 1.08 g of aluminium combined to 0.96 g of oxygen.

2. Calculate the empirical formula of the hydrocarbon containing 0.60 g of carbon and 0.15 g of hydrogen.

3. Calculate the empirical formula for the compound containing 6.21 g of lead combined to 7.62 g of iodine.

4. 6.40 g of iron oxide was found to contain 4.48 g of iron. Calculate the empirical formula for the iron oxide.

5. Calculate the percentage of hydrogen in ammonium nitrate, NH_4NO_3.

6. Calculate the percentage of oxygen in ammonium nitrate, NH_4NO_3.

7. Calculate the percentage of hydrogen in water.

8. Calculate the percentage of sulphur in sulphur dioxide.

Answers 1. Al_2O_3 **2.** CH_3 **3.** PbI_2 **4.** Fe_2O_3 **5.** 5% **6.** 60% **7.** 11.1% **8.** 50%

Calculations from a balanced equation

Key Facts
- To calculate how much of a product is made, the equation for a reaction can be used.
- The equation for a reaction can also be used to calculate how much reactant should be used.

Calculating the mass of products

The **equation** for a reaction can be used to **calculate** how much product is made.

Example

What **mass** of water is produced when **8 g** of **hydrogen** is burned in **oxygen**?

RAM of H = 1

RAM of O = 16

Write out the balanced equation:

$$2H_2(g) + O_2(g) \rightarrow 2H_2O(g)$$

Work out the formula mass:

$$2 \times (1 \times 2) + (16 \times 2) \rightarrow 2 \times (18)$$
$$4 + 32 \rightarrow 36$$

So 4 g of hydrogen will make 36 g of water.

What does 1 g of hydrogen make?

1 g of hydrogen makes $\frac{36}{4}$ = 9 g of water

Multiply by the number of grams:

8 g of hydrogen makes $9 \times 8 = 72$ g of water.

This calculation shows that if 8 g of hydrogen is burned in oxygen, 72 g of H_2O is made.

Calculating the mass of reactants

The equation for a reaction can also be used to calculate how much reactant should be used.

Example

What **mass** of magnesium should be used to produce **60 g** of magnesium oxide?

RAM of Mg = 24.5

RAM of O = 16

Write out the balanced equation:

$$2Mg(s) + O_2(g) \rightarrow 2MgO(s)$$

Work out the formula masses and the reacting quantities:

$(2 \times 24.5) + (2 \times 16) \rightarrow 2MgO$

$49 + 32 \rightarrow 81$

81 g of MgO is made from 49 g of Mg.

How much is needed to make 1 g of MgO?

1 g of MgO is made from $\frac{49}{81}$ g of Mg.

Multiply by the number of grams:

60 g of MgO is made from $\frac{49}{81} \times 60$ g = 36.3 g

This calculation shows that to produce 60 g of MgO, 36.3 g of Mg should be used.

Quick Test

1. Calculate the mass of water produced when 0.2 g of hydrogen is burned in air.

2. Calculate the mass of hydrogen needed to produce 0.72 g of water.

3. Calculate the mass of calcium oxide formed when 10 g of calcium carbonate decomposes as in the equation, $CaCO_3 \rightarrow CaO + CO_2$

4. The equation for calcium burning in oxygen is $2Ca(s) + O_2(g) \rightarrow 2CaO(s)$
Calculate the mass of calcium required to produce 1.12 g of calcium oxide.

Answers 1. 1.8 g **2.** 0.08 g **3.** 5.6 g **4.** 0.80 g

Types of reactions

The following is a summary of different types of reactions you need to know in Standard Grade Chemistry.

- **Addition** – When a molecule such as hydrogen or bromine 'adds on' across the double $C=C$ bond in an unsaturated hydrocarbon such as ethene.

- **Addition Polymerisation** – When unsaturated monomers join to form a larger molecule known as a polymer by opening their carbon-to-carbon double bonds and linking together.

- **Combustion** – the chemical name for burning. When something burns it reacts with oxygen. If there is not enough oxygen present, **incomplete combustion** may take place.

- **Condensation** – when small molecules join together to make a larger molecule and water is produced.

- **Condensation Polymerisation** – When small molecules, known as monomers, join together to form a larger molecule known as a polymer and water is produced where these molecules link.

- **Corrosion** – When the surface of a metal changes from an element to a compound. In the case of iron this is called rusting. Since a metal loses electrons when it corrodes, corrosion is an example of an oxidation reaction.

- **Cracking** – Breaking large hydrocarbon molecules into smaller molecules which are more useful and more in demand. At least one of the products is unsaturated (contains a double $C=C$ bond).

- **Displacement** – When a metal higher in the electrochemical series takes the place of a metal lower in the electrochemical series. A displacement reaction involves both oxidation and reduction and so is also a redox reaction.

- **Exothermic** – A reaction in which energy is given out. Many different reactions are exothermic, but you should make a point of remembering that combustion and neutralisation are both exothermic.

- **Endothermic** – A reaction in which energy is taken in. Two good examples of endothermic reactions are nitrogen and oxygen reacting together during lightning storms and photosynthesis.

- **Fermentation** – This is the reaction in which sugars are converted into alcohol and carbon dioxide using enzymes found in yeast.

- **Hydrolysis** – Breaking down a large molecule into smaller molecules in the presence of water. Hydrolysis is the reverse of condensation.

- **Neutralisation** – when an acid and a base cancel each other out. Examples of bases include alkalis, metal oxides and metal carbonates.

- **Oxidation** – originally the name given when something reacts with oxygen. Usually an oxidation reaction involves the loss of electrons. (Try to remember **OIL** meaning **O**xidation **I**s **L**oss (of electrons)).

- **Photosynthesis** – The reaction in which plants convert carbon dioxide and water into glucose and water. Light energy and chlorophyll are also required.

- **Precipitation** – When two liquids are mixed together and an insoluble solid is made. The solid formed is called the precipitate.

- **Polymerisation** – The reaction in which small molecules called monomers join together to form larger molecules known as polymers. The two types of polymerisation are **addition polymerisation** and **condensation polymerisation**.

- **Redox** – A term to describe both oxidation and reduction which both take place at the same time.

- **Reduction** – a gain of electrons. (Try to remember **RIG** meaning **R**eduction **I**s **G**ain (of electrons)). Oxidation and reduction are the reverse of each other.

- **Respiration** – The reaction in which oxygen combines with glucose in living organisms to release energy. Carbon dioxide and water are also formed. Respiration is the reverse of photosynthesis.

Index